At Marriott Senior Living Services, we understand the challenges that arise as family members age, and the concern that can accompany these changes. We also recognize that living independently is the key to health and happiness. In our senior living communities, our philosophy is to offer choices to individuals, so they can remain as independent as possible for as long as possible. As one of the nation's leaders in senior living since 1984, we offer our residents many different levels of care, including independent living, assisted living, nursing and rehabilitative care, and special care centers for people with Alzheimer's disease and related memory disorders.

We are dedicated to working with families to create a safe, caring and stimulating environment for our residents. Families of our residents benefit from knowing their loved ones are being cared for by an experienced, well-trained staff. By continually listening and responding to our customers, we have earned a reputation for quality in senior living.

In this spirit, we are pleased to offer this special edition of a wonderful and informative book, *How to Care for Aging Parents*. We hope this book provides valuable and practical information to help in caring for your loved one. We welcome the opportunity to be of further assistance as you explore various alternatives.

Bill Marriott
Chairman and CEO
Marriott International, Inc.

THE MARRIOTT FAMILY OF SENIOR LIVING COMMUNITIES

Marriott Senior Living Services is the nation's leading provider of quality senior housing. There are more than 150 communities across the country with others in development or under construction. For more information, please visit our website at www.marriottseniorliving.com.

ALABAMA
Birmingham,
Galleria Oaks Guest
Home
(205)823-2393
B

ARIZONA
Chandler,
Village Oaks at
Chandler
(480) 855-6500
B

Glendale,
Village Oaks at
Glendale
(602)938-7166
B

Mesa,
Village Oaks at Mesa
(480)964-8788
B

Peoria,
The Forum at
Desert Harbor
(623)972-0995
ABC

Scottsdale,
Brighton Gardens
(480)941-2222
BC

Scottsdale,
The Forum at
Pueblo Norte
(480)948-3990
ABC

Sun City,
Brighton Gardens
(623)933-2222
BC

Tucson,
The Forum at
Tucson
(520)325-4800
ABCD

ARKANSAS
Little Rock,
Pleasant Hills
(501)225-9405
AB

CALIFORNIA
Carlsbad,
Brighton Gardens
(760)720-9898
BCD

Camarillo,
Brighton Gardens
(805)388-8086
BCD

Cupertino,
The Forum at
Rancho San Antonio
(650)944-0100
ABC

Hemet,
Marriott MapleRidge
(909)929-5988
BD

Laguna Creek,
Marriott MapleRidge
(916)683-1881
BD

Laguna Hills,
Villa Valencia
(949)581-6111
ABC

Northridge
Brighton Gardens
(800)881-3131
BD

Palm Springs,
Marriott MapleRidge
(760)322-3444
BD

Rancho Mirage,
Brighton Gardens
(760)340-5999
BCD

San Diego,
Brighton Gardens
(858)259-2222
BCD

San Diego,
Remington Club
(858)673-6300
ABC

San Dimas,
Brighton Gardens,
(909)394-0304
BCD

San Juan Capistrano,
Brighton Gardens
(949)248-8855
BCD

Santa Rosa,
Brighton Gardens
(707)566-8600
BCD

Yorba Linda,
Brighton Gardens
(714)777-9666
BCD

COLORADO
Colorado Springs,
Brighton Gardens
(719)329-1774
BCD

Denver,
Brighton Gardens
(303)671-2500
BCD

Lakewood,
Brighton Gardens
(303)237-5700
BCD

CONNECTICUT
Stamford,
Brighton Gardens
(203)322-2100
BD

Stamford,
Edgehill
(203)323-2323
ABC

Woodbridge,
Brighton Gardens
(203)389-2911
BD

DELAWARE
Newark,
Millcroft
(302)366-0160
ABC

Wilmington,
Forwood Manor
(302)529-1600
ABC

Wilmington,
Foulk Manor North
(302)478-4296
ABC

Wilmington,
Foulk Manor South
(302)655-6249
BCD

Wilmington,
Shipley Manor
(302)479-0111
ABC

FLORIDA
Boca Raton,
Stratford Court
(561)392-2772
ABCD

Boynton Beach,
Brighton Gardens
(561)369-7919
BC

Coral Springs,
Park Summit
(954)752-9500
ABC

Deerfield Beach,
The Forum at
Deer Creek
(954)698-6269
ABC

Deerfield Beach,
Horizon Club
(954)481-2304
AB

Fort Lauderdale,
Tiffany House
(954)563-3116
B

Fort Myers,
Calusa Harbour
(941)332-3333
ABC

Fort Myers,
Springwood Court
(941)278-0078
B

Jacksonville,
Village Oaks at
Orange Park
(904)264-0207
B

Jacksonville,
Village Oaks at
Southpoint
(904)296-2384
B

Maitland,
Brighton Gardens
(407)645-3990
BC

Melbourne,
Village Oaks at
Melbourne
(321)733-7111
B

Naples,
Brighton Gardens
(941)566-8077
BC

Orlando,
Village Oaks at Conway
(407)277-7225
B

Orlando,
Village Oaks at
Tuskawilla
(407)699-7999
B

Palm Harbor,
Coral Oaks
(727)787-3333
AB

Palm Harbor,
Stratford Court
(727)787-1500
ABC

Port St. Lucie,
Brighton Gardens
(561)335-9990
BC

Tampa,
Brighton Gardens
(813)908-2333
BCD

Venice,
Brighton Gardens
(941)484-8801
BC

West Palm Beach,
Brighton Gardens
(561)686-5100
BCD

West Palm Beach,
Fountainview
(561)697-5500
AB

GEORGIA
Atlanta,
Brighton Gardens
of Buckhead
(404)846-8335
BD

Atlanta,
Brighton Gardens
of Dunwoody
(770)730-9333
BD

Vinings,
Brighton Gardens
(770)435-4477
BD

ILLINOIS
Arlington Heights,
Church Creek
(847)506-3200
AC

Burr Ridge,
Brighton Gardens
(630)920-2900
BC

Hoffman Estates,
Brighton Gardens
(847)755-0735
BD

Orland Park,
Brighton Gardens
(708)403-2001
BD

Prospect Heights,
Brighton Gardens
(847)797-2700
BC

St. Charles,
Brighton Gardens
(630)587-6120
BD

Wheaton,
Brighton Gardens
(630)681-1234
BD

INDIANA
Fort Wayne,
Village Oaks
(219)484-0308
B

Indianapolis,
Village Oaks
(317)889-9822
BD

Indianapolis,
The Forum at the
Crossing
(317)257-7406
ABCD

Indianapolis,
Meridian Oaks Guest
Home
(317)575-9200
B

KANSAS
Overland Park,
The Forum at
Overland Park
(913)648-4500
ABC

Prairie Village,
Brighton Gardens
(913)262-1611
BCD

KENTUCKY
Edgewood,
Brighton Gardens
(859)426-1888
BD*

Lexington,
Lafayette at Country
Place
(859)259-1331
AB*

Lexington,
Lexington Country Place
(859)259-3486
C*

Louisville,
Forum at Brookside
(502)245-3048
AC*

MARYLAND
Bethesda,
Maplewood Park
Place
(301)530-0500
ABC

Chevy Chase,
Brighton Gardens
at Friendship Heights
(301)656-1900
BD

Columbia,
Brighton Gardens
(410)884-0773
BD

No. Bethesda,
Brighton Gardens of
Tuckerman Lane
(301)897-8566
BC

Pikesville,
Brighton Gardens
(410)580-0892
BD

Silver Spring,
Bedford Court
(301)598-2900
ABC

Towson,
Brighton Gardens
(410)377-2100
BD

MASSACHUSETTS
Danvers,
Brighton Gardens of
the North Shore
(978)777-5717
BD

Dartmouth,
Marriott MapleRidge
(508)999-0404
BD

Dedham,
Brighton Gardens
(781)407-7711
BD

Plymouth,
Marriott MapleRidge
(508)746-9733
BD

Winchester,
The Gables at
Winchester
(781)756-1026
AB

MICHIGAN
Northville,
Brighton Gardens
(734)420-7917
BD

NEBRASKA
Omaha,
Brighton Gardens
(402)393-7313
BCD

NEVADA
Las Vegas,
Brighton Gardens
(702)617-1260
BCD

Las Vegas,
Village Oaks
at Las Vegas
(702)451-7896
B

NEW JERSEY
Cherry Hill,
Brighton Gardens
(856)424-7227
BD

Edison,
Brighton Gardens
(732)767-1031
BC

LEGEND

A– Independent Full-Service—Seniors enjoy an active, fulfilling lifestyle without worrying about household maintenance. Services include daily meals, weekly housekeeping and linen services, scheduled local transportation, and a 24-hour medical alert system.

B– Assisted Living—Designed for seniors who need some assis-tance with daily activities such as bathing, dressing, and medica-tion reminders. The focus at these communities is on wellness and keeping residents as independent as possible by providing a per-sonalized plan of assistance.

C– Nursing Care—Our nursing care centers emphasize the contributions and dignity of each individual. We offer a variety of nursing care and support services, including 24-hour skilled nursing care, post hospital and post surgical care, restorative care, physician services, pharmacy services, and family counseling.

D– Alzheimer's Care—Appropriate for people with Alzheimer's or other memory disorders, we offer a unique approach to caring that can restore quality lives of residents as well as to their caregivers. Our Life Enrichment program offers a variety of activities including exercise, crafts, local outings, counseling, and support groups.

*Licensed Personal Care

Florham Park,
Brighton Gardens
(937)966-8999
BD

Lakewood,
Leisure Park
(732)370-0444
ABCD

Middletown,
Brighton Gardens
(732)275-0790
BD

Mountainside,
Brighton Gardens
(908)654-4460
BD

Paramus,
Brighton Gardens
(201)251-9600
BD

Saddle River,
Brighton Gardens
(201)818-8680
BD

West Orange,
Brighton Gardens
(973)731-9840
BD

NEVADA
Las Vegas,
Brighton Gardens
(702)617-1260
BCD

NEW MEXICO
Albuquerque,
The Montebello on
Academy
(505)294-9944
ABC

NEW YORK
Port Washington,
Harbor Ridge
(516)625-7300
AC

NORTH CAROLINA
Charlotte,
Brighton Gardens
(704)643-1400
BD

Greensboro,
Brighton Gardens
(336)297-4700
BD

Raleigh,
Brighton Gardens
(919)571-1123
BD

Winston-Salem,
Brighton Gardens
(336)722-2224
BD

OHIO
Cincinnati,
Brighton Gardens
(513)792-9697
BD

Columbus,
The Forum at
Knightsbridge
(614)451-6793
ABCD

Dayton,
Brighton Gardens of
Washington Township
(937)438-0054
BD

Westlake,
Brighton Gardens
(440)808-0074
BD

Willoughby,
Marriott MapleRidge
(440)269-8600
BD

OKLAHOMA
Oklahoma City,
Brighton Gardens
(405)748-6464
BD

Tulsa,
Brighton Gardens
(918)743-2700
BD

PENNSYLVANIA
Haverford,
The Quadrangle
(610)642-3000
ABCD

SOUTH CAROLINA
Greenville,
Brighton Gardens
(864)286-6600
BCD

Myrtle Beach,
Myrtle Beach Manor
(843)449-5283
BCD

TENNESSEE
Brentwood,
Brighton Gardens
(615)376-5299
BD

Memphis,
Brighton Gardens
(901)763-3232
BD

Memphis,
Kirby Oaks Guest
Home
(901)362-6257
B

TEXAS
Austin,
Brighton Gardens
(512)418-8822
BC

Austin,
Duval Oaks Guest
Home
(512)418-8228
B

Bellaire,
Brighton Gardens
(713)665-3888
BC

Dallas,
Brighton Gardens
(972)661-3111
B

Dallas,
The Forum at
Park Lane
(214)369-9902
ABC

Dallas,
Kingsley Oaks Guest
Home
(214)343-7445
B

El Paso,
The MonteVista at
Coronado
(915)833-2229
ACD

El Paso,
Village Oaks at
Cielo Vista
(915)772-4036
B

Farmers Branch,
Village Oaks at
Farmers Branch
(972)241-3955
B

Ft. Worth,
Tanglewood Oaks
Guest Home
(817)922-9559
B

Houston,
Champion Oaks
Guest Home
(281)440-0966
B

Houston,
The Forum at
Memorial Woods
(713)956-0870
ABCD

Houston,
Memorial Oaks
Guest Home
(713)782-3355
B

Houston,
Sugar Land Oaks
Guest Home
(281)491-6257
B

Plano,
Collin Oaks Guest
Home
(972)519-0480
B

San Antonio,
Brighton Gardens
(210)930-1040
BC

San Antonio,
The Forum at
Lincoln Heights
(210)824-2314
ABC

San Antonio,
Northwest Oaks
Guest Home
(210)641-6257
B

San Antonio,
Village Oaks at
Hollywood Park
(210)495-9340
B

Woodlands,
The Forum at the
Woodlands
(281)292-2600
AB

UTAH
Salt Lake City,
Brighton Gardens
(801)359-0050
BCD

VIRGINIA
Arlington,
Brighton Gardens
(703)294-6875
BD

Arlington,
The Jefferson
(703)516-9455
ABCD

Charlottesville,
The Colonnades
(804)963-4198
ABC

Fort Belvoir,
The Fairfax
(703)799-1200
ABC

Richmond,
Brighton Gardens
(804)741-8880
BD

Virginia Beach
Brighton Gardens
(757)499-4800
B

WASHINGTON
Bellevue,
Brighton Gardens
(425)401-0300
BD

Lynnwood,
Hearthside
(425)771-7700
BD

Snohomish,
Hearthside
(360)568-1900
BD

SPECIAL ABRIDGED EDITION

HOW TO CARE for AGING PARENTS

VIRGINIA MORRIS

SELECTED CHAPTERS BROUGHT TO YOU BY:

WORKMAN PUBLISHING • NEW YORK

GET READY, GET SET

Talking With Your Parent • Beyond Denial • Gathering Essential Documents • Organizing Your Own Life

....

N O ONE PLANS TO TAKE CARE OF A PARENT. WE DON'T set aside money or time for the task, or begin reading books such as this one as soon as a parent turns 65. For the most part, a parent's old age, and the needs and dilemmas that typically accompany it, come as a surprise. In fact, even when events begin to unfold, and the reality of the situation becomes apparent, most of us still look the other way, hoping that perhaps things will take care of themselves, that Dad will be all right and our services will not be needed. As a result, we react to each crisis only as it arises.

So here's some advice that's not easy to hear, but truly invaluable to heed: Think ahead and prepare yourself and your parent for what may come. If your father's arthritis is getting worse, talk with him about what might happen if he can no longer manage alone, and start exploring community programs and services that he might need. If your mother has Alzheimer's, learn her wishes concerning her future care and understand and tour all the options available. Get a jump on this.

This point can't be stressed enough. Delaying, postponing or looking the other way is a natural, but risky, approach to take. Your parent will grow older, his health will fail, his needs will intensify. Staying one page ahead, one day ahead, one question ahead, will give you and your parent time to consider the options carefully. It will ensure that your parent receives the best care possible. And, while it may not seem so now, it will provide you with a little peace of mind—a priceless commodity during such times.

Critical Conversations

Although it can become too late quite suddenly, it is never too soon to talk to your parent about the future—her medical care, housing, finances and personal concerns. Obviously if your mother has been diagnosed with cancer or emphysema, these talks are urgent. But even if she is still relatively healthy and independent, discussing her future is vital. Many preparations, such as buying long-term care insurance or getting on a waiting list for an assisted living residence or nursing home, must be done well in advance. And you need to know how she wants things handled if she grows too sick or frail to handle them on her own.

Discussing the future also helps prepare your family emotionally for what may come. If your father is encouraged now to explore the possibility of moving out of his house, it will be easier for him to make the move if it becomes necessary. And these talks give your parent and family members a chance to air their worries and anxieties, to reassure one another, and to learn the truth about any haunting questions. If your mother has been diagnosed with cancer, for example, she may be secretly terrified that she will be in constant pain or be left to die alone in a hospital room. When you create a context within which she can voice such concerns, you can help her learn about pain control and explore various in-home nursing services. And she can be reassured that you will be there for her throughout the time that remains.

YOUR RELUCTANCE

Admittedly, asking about your father's personal finances or anticipating a time when he can no longer live alone is not easy. You may have firmly established a relationship over the years in which these personal issues were never discussed. Raising them now may upset that fragile, but relatively comfortable, balance. If he is a domineering or protective force in your life, you risk losing— at least for a moment—the role of the child, a role that may frustrate you, but may also make you feel safe. Furthermore, initiating a conversation about your parent's finances, health care or housing opens you up to new responsibilities—you brought it up, so now you have to find some answers—and it forces you, and perhaps your parent, to recognize his mortality.

Certain issues may make you particularly uncomfortable. For example, you may be reluctant to ask about assets and wills out of respect for your parent's privacy or out of fear of sounding like a gold-digger. Or you may not want to bring up the subject of death for fear of upsetting your parent. But the truth is that your parent and other family members probably share your concerns as well as your reluctance to discuss them. In fact, your mother may be keeping silent because she is worried about upsetting *you*. Your breaking open the dam and initiating discussions about these taboo subjects is likely to be a welcome relief for all concerned.

Think about your reluctance and the reasons for it. Contemplate your role and the risks of both talking and failing to talk. Remember, as awkward as it may be, talking about the worst case scenarios won't make them come true, and refusing to talk about them won't make them go away. Ignoring the inevitable will only leave you unprepared for a crisis.

FINDING THE WORDS

If you can't come right out and say what you want to, use an indirect approach. For example, you might express your concern about a friend or family member who is seriously ill or describe your own financial situation and plans to draft a will. Or, use a magazine article or television show as a springboard. *I was reading an article on long-term care insurance. Do you have this kind of insurance, Dad?* If your father had elderly parents, ask how he handled certain matters for them.

If talking face-to-face is too awkward, write a list of questions for your mother. Tell her these are some issues you've been concerned about and ask her to think about them. Then plan a time to sit down with her and discuss them.

YOUR PARENT'S DENIAL

When your parent is hiding behind denial—*Oh, honey, why do you have to bring up such dreadful things? Let's talk about something more pleasant*—grant her some of that protection. Be patient and try to understand her fears and the reasons why she might not want to face the facts. If the subject isn't pressing, simply ask her to think about the matter and then bring it up another day. Sometimes things have to reach a crisis before such discussions are possible.

When things do reach a critical state and denial becomes an obstacle—when your parent refuses to consider vital legal documents even after months of chemotherapy or refuses to see that her bank account is almost dry—then you need to push, tenderly and compassionately, but very firmly. *Mom, we cannot ignore this any longer. We have got to deal with it.*

If you are still not successful, ask another family member to talk with her. For whatever reasons, she may be more receptive with some-

BREAKING THE SILENCE

❖ Raise any discussions about your parent's health, finances or other matters at a time when you won't be interrupted, and when you and your parent are calm and rested.

❖ Be open and very clear with the facts—a poor medical prognosis, a major financial hurdle, a less-than-optimal selection of housing options. Don't hide information to protect your father. Lies or half-truths will only hurt him in the long run.

❖ If your mother changes the subject or makes it clear that she doesn't want to talk about something, back off and try again another time.

❖ Keep the discussion focused on your father and his concerns. *You* may worry about who is going to take care of him once the Parkinson's disease gets worse, but *he* may be frightened about becoming helpless, losing people's respect or becoming a burden. You may be surprised to find that your mother has been worried about your well-being should something happen to her. Give her ample room to express her thoughts, for these are important issues that need your undivided attention.

❖ Whenever possible, phrase your concerns as questions, letting your parent draw the conclusions and make the choices. Ask what she thinks should be done rather than telling her what should be done.

❖ Listen carefully, even when you have firm convictions about what's feasible. You may have ideas about where your mother should live or how she should handle her finances, but it's particularly important to listen now. Be open-minded and make a point of really listening to her preferences, and letting her know that you hear and understand.

❖ End each discussion before you or your parent becomes tired or cranky.

❖ Leave the conversation open. One discussion breaks the ice, but these topics need to be discussed repeatedly. Ask your parent to think about whatever subject you have been discussing and conclude the conversation by saying that you'd like to continue the talk in a week or so.

one else. Or urge her to visit a clergyman, a social worker, a lawyer or a doctor to discuss these matters. It's often easier to talk to and accept the advice of someone outside the family circle, especially if the other person is a trusted professional.

If, no matter what you do, your parent continues to deny the facts, you may have to let things be. You cannot force her to act on matters that she simply is not willing to face. But you should have a plan in mind anyway. Think about what will happen if your mother becomes seriously ill or dependent. What help might she need? How much will you be able to give? And where will the rest of the help (services, support, etc.) come from? Who will pay for it? Try to involve siblings as much as possible in planning for future eventualities.

If your father's denial gets in the way of specific actions that absolutely must be taken—he refuses to stop driving even though his vision is very poor, or he won't see a doctor even though his leg is swollen—then you may have to step in and take action, regardless of his wishes.

WHAT TO TALK ABOUT

You may know you need to have this discussion with Dad, you may have dealt with your own denial— but where do you begin and what do you ask? Here are a few questions to get you started.

◆ **Your parent's needs and concerns.** What are your parent's biggest worries about the future? What goals in his life does he feel are unmet, what tasks unfinished or conflicts unresolved? What aspects of his life are most important to him at this stage of life? Being near family, hearing the opera, seeing certain friends, practicing his religion?

◆ **Housing.** How important is it to your parent to remain in his

After my father died I was very worried about my mom's finances. My dad always took care of everything that had to do with money. Mom never knew about his accounts; I don't think she ever balanced the checkbook.

I said to Mom over and over, 'Let's review your financial situation,' and I offered repeatedly to take care of her bills for her. She would say, 'Brenda, don't worry about it. I'm fine.' And then she would change the subject.

Then my brother came to visit and within a day he had Mom pulling out folders and showing him bank statements. By the time he left she had handed over almost all of her financial stuff to him.

I was stunned. I mean, I was glad to have it settled, but I was also a little annoyed. I'm an accountant. He's a teacher. I guess she feels that money is men's work. I probably should have thought to get him involved right from the start.
—BRENDA S.

THREE CRUCIAL DOCUMENTS

Whatever else you do, be sure your parent has, or has at least considered:

❖ **An updated and valid will** which ensures that his belongings (no matter how extensive or meager) will be allocated according to his wishes. A current will reduces the likelihood of family conflict and an extended and complicated probate process.

❖ **A durable power of attorney** which allows a designated person to make legally binding decisions for your parent, from signing checks to making housing choices, should he become incapacitated. Having power of attorney means the family can avoid the harrowing process of going to court to have a guardian named to oversee his care and finances.

❖ **Advance directives** (a living will and durable power of attorney for health care) which specify your parent's wishes concerning medical care and name someone to make decisions in his stead, should he become incompetent.

own home? Where would he want to live if he could no longer manage at home? What if it isn't possible for him to live with other family members?

◆ **Financial and legal matters.** What are your parent's current financial needs and potential future needs? Is he in a financial position to meet these needs? Is his insurance—including life, health, home and auto insurance—adequate and current? Has he executed all necessary legal papers and are they up-to-date? (See box, above.)

◆ **Health care.** Does your parent have a good doctor whom she trusts? If she is sick, what is her prognosis and how will that affect her housing, finances and care? If

you had to make medical decisions for her, what would she want you to know? Does she dread the prospect of a particular disability (dementia, blindness, paralysis)? If so, why? Is she more apprehensive about being in pain or about being groggy from painkillers? Is there a certain point after which she would no longer want aggressive medical care? How does she feel about hospice care?

◆ **Death and funerals.** This may be the toughest subject for you to discuss, but it may be the one foremost on your parent's mind. Try to bring it up, however obliquely, and see if he is willing to talk about it. What, if anything, frightens him about dying? Is he more frightened about death or about what the end of his life will be like? Is there a way that you might be able to alleviate some of his fears? What are his religious beliefs about death? What kind of service does he want? Does he want to be buried or cremated? Has he made any advance arrangements for his burial or funeral?

Gathering Information

As your mother grows increasingly frail, your family will need certain financial records and other information such as insurance policies, advance directives and the names of her doctors. (See Checklist on the following page.) Find out whether your parent has all the relevant papers and make sure that you or another family member knows where they are.

If both of your parents are alive, you might simply remind them that these papers are important and suggest that they get them in order and that each has full access to them. If only one of your parents is alive, you might offer some help in finding these documents. If she doesn't want help, impress upon her the importance of gathering these materials, and then follow up later to make sure that she has done it.

If your parent is infirm and you are looking for these papers without his help, you may become shocked or embarrassed as you hunt through his personal papers. If so, get a sibling or friend to help, and

FALLING ON DEAF EARS

Talking about these issues may not be a problem; getting your parent to heed any advice, however, may be extremely frustrating. You know your mother should sign a will. You are certain that your father should move out of his house. But he refuses to budge. What could possibly be more maddening than a parent who simply won't listen?

You may need to step in regardless of your parent's wishes if the situation is truly dire, but it's more likely that you need to do something far more difficult: Accept your parent's autonomy, and appreciate the limits of your control over his life. You may be convinced that he's making a mistake, but unless he is in real danger, your parent has a right to take risks and make foolish decisions. One day you will have the same rights, despite the better judgment of others.

do it on a schedule that is manageable for you—all at once, like swallowing a pill, or in a series of small doses.

Call your parent's lawyer, accountant or anyone else who has or has had a hand in your parent's financial or legal affairs. Then look

CHECKLIST

Documents and information that your parent needs

❑ Names, addresses and phone numbers of:
- —doctors, dentists and other medical providers, such as optometrists, hearing aid suppliers and pharmacists
- —lawyers, financial advisors and accountants, insurance agents, real estate agents
- —banks and other financial institutions

❑ Your parent's will and codicils (amendments) to the will, as well as his health care proxy, living will and durable power of attorney

❑ The keys to safe-deposit boxes and post office boxes

❑ The location of any hidden valuables

❑ Insurance policies, including life, health, disability, mortgage or loan, homeowner's, accident, auto and credit card

❑ Social security, Medicare and Medicaid numbers and identification cards

❑ Any rental agreements or other business contracts

❑ A complete list of your parent's assets, including
- —savings, checking and money market accounts
- —stocks, bonds and other securities
- —deeds to all real estate
- —titles to automobiles, boats and other vehicles
- —business ownership and partnership agreements
- —profit-sharing and pension plans
- —retirement accounts (IRA, Keogh, SEP, etc.)

❑ A list of debts, including mortgages and other loans, credit card debts, outstanding bills and other liabilities

❑ A list of all routine household bills, such as utilities bills and insurance premiums, that you may have to take care of if your parent becomes ill

❑ Any appraisals of personal property

❑ Copies of federal and state tax returns from the past three to five years

❑ Receipts from property taxes and other large recent payments

❑ Records of any personal loans your parent may have made to family members, business associates or others in the obvious places—a safe-deposit box, desk and bureau drawers, office files and papers stacked on tables and in corners. If you don't find everything you need, look for leads, such as bills, canceled checks, receipts, address books and letters.

Insurance companies will often provide information about a policy even when the request comes from a family member of the insured. The social security office, former employers and the local office of veterans' affairs may be willing to send you information about pensions and other benefits. Unfortunately, banks are not very helpful in these situations unless you are dealing with a local bank where the manager knows your family. By law, banks can give out account information only to the owner of the account or the owner's legal guardian.

The Key Is Organization

If you diligently write lists of "Things to Do" on scraps of paper and then routinely misplace them, or if you're constantly remembering things that you shouldn't have forgotten but did:

◆ Keep a tiny spiral notebook in your purse or back pocket at all times. When you think of an essential errand while driving to the grocery store, jot it down at the next traffic light. As a reward for your efforts, you get to cross things off as you accomplish them. Re-

member, if this book is left at home on your desk, it will be of little use to you.

◆ Have a pocket calendar on your desk or by your kitchen phone (or get one that travels in your purse or briefcase). Record not just the obvious dates and appointments, but every task that must be done on a certain day. If bottles and cans get picked up every other Thursday morning for recycling, make a note to yourself to put them out on Wednesday night. With so much on your mind now, sometimes

"During my mother's illness, I accumulated so much stuff—brochures from nursing homes, documents from lawyers, forms from Medicare, pamphlets from social service agencies. Every time I got something, I just tossed it into this giant box in my bedroom. Then whenever something came up, like when I wanted to get meals delivered to her while I was away, I would think, 'Oh yeah, I have something on that,' but I could never find it.

A friend came over one day and dumped out my box and started sorting through it. She spent the entire day organizing the whole mess. That was the best thing anyone did for me during those two years. Not only could I find things quickly, but it made me feel better. I'd been feeling so out of control, and that gave me a little edge. It made an enormous difference."
—TERRY B.

remembering your own name can be an effort.

♦ Likewise, each time you call a home-care agency, a lawyer or a social worker, make a note about the call on your calendar, including the name of the person you spoke with and what you talked about, so you can refer to it later if necessary. *(But I spoke to Anne Preston on March 18 and she confirmed that the home health aide would start tomorrow.)*

♦ Whenever you make calls to agencies, doctors, etc., have all the necessary information in front of you and have all of your questions written out. Otherwise you may forget an important question and have to go through all the secretaries and recorded announcements to make contact again. Get into the habit of asking for people's direct lines or extension numbers.

♦ Confirm, confirm. It's better to confirm an appointment the day before than to find out that your father's hearing aid specialist has taken an unscheduled vacation and his temporary assistant forgot to cancel his appointments.

♦ Buy some folders and a sturdy file box or an accordion file, and use it to store all information regarding your parent's care. Label each folder or section in a way that makes sense to you—Medical Information, Nursing Home Brochures, Legal Papers, Community Resources, Letters to Siblings, etc. If you hate to throw things out (you never know when you might need it), keep a file called Information No Longer Needed, or Trash File, just so your other files are current and not overstuffed.

Once you have your files set up, use them. Keep them up-to-date rather than just stacking papers in a "to be filed" pile.

♦ Make a master list of all essential names and phone numbers and store one copy at the beginning of the file box and one copy beside the telephone. (If you're calling certain people or agencies regularly, and if your telephone has a memory feature, you might want to store their numbers into your automatic dialing system.)

♦ If you work better on a computer, set up a computer file that includes all the information and accounts concerning your parent. Be sure to make a back-up disc copy, and keep it in a safe place.

♦ If you're handling your parent's finances or housing, make copies of all medical receipts, insurance claims, nursing home applications and other important documents so that you always have a record of anything that is in the works.

♦ Write a daily schedule. Before scoffing at this idea, try it for a couple of weeks. You may not adhere to it precisely, but it will help structure your day so you are not constantly thinking, "I've got to get to the cleaners. I've got to call the social security office." The task—or the breather you need—will already be assigned to a time slot. Even if you don't use it, writing a schedule for a few weeks will help you to see where your day is going and why you don't have time for all the things you need to do. And it may give you ideas for how you can be more efficient. For example:

7 a.m.	shower, get everyone moving
8	breakfast
8:45	take Mom to the eye doctor for 9 a.m. appointment, read newspaper in the waiting room
10	drop Mom at day care, pick up Bob's pants at tailor
10:30-11:30	exercise class
12	lunch with Ed Farmer
1:30-5 p.m.	work on Copeland report—no interruptions!
5	pick up Mom at day care and get last-minute groceries
6	fix dinner
7	dinner is served
8	help Mom get ready for bed
8:30	pay bills
9	call Wendy for a chat
10	watch Picket Fences
11	bed

Be reasonable when making your schedule. Give yourself more than the minimum time required to do a chore or to get someplace. If you have an appointment, expect to wait. If a recipe says 30 minutes, give yourself 45. And finally, if you're a morning scrambler, get up 15 minutes earlier than usual to give yourself time to organize the day and start it off calmly.

ORGANIZING FROM A DISTANCE

When you are caring for your parent from a distance it's even more important to be organized because you have to accomplish tasks during visits or by phone. Whenever you visit, take a mental inventory of your parent's health and living situation and try to foresee trouble before it happens. Does your mother seem wobbly or dizzy? Is the house tidy and clean? Is she well-groomed, or has her personal hygiene deteriorated? Is there ample food in the refrigerator and is it fresh? Are there piles of unopened mail or unpaid bills? If things are askew it may be a sign of serious trouble—depression, confusion, poor appetite because of an illness—or simply a signal to you that she needs some outside help at home.

Establish a support network as soon as possible. Make a list of friends, family or neighbors who live near your parent, people you can call in case of trouble. Also learn about local services such as volunteer visitors, homemakers, adult day care and meal delivery programs.

Organize your visits in advance so you can accomplish as much as possible. If you need to meet with doctors, lawyers, social workers or other professionals, try to set up appointments a month ahead, as their schedules get filled up quickly. Be sure to confirm these appointments closer to the date. Include some time during your visit to talk with nearby relatives or others involved in your parent's care.

Other tips for caring from afar:

♦ When you can't be there, find someone who can. See if a relative, friend or neighbor will stop by occasionally to check on your parent, or contact a visitor service, home-

A FEW GOOD NUMBERS

Get some basic information about local services, housing options and legal matters early —before your parent or you need to use them. With just a few quick calls you can find out much of what you need to know and get leads to other agencies.

❖ **The "area agency on aging,"** which can be found by calling the Eldercare Locator (800-677-1116) or the state unit on aging, has information about services and programs available in your parent's community and may be able to answer specific questions about your parent's care.

❖ **The state long-term care ombudsman's office,** which represents residents of nursing homes and their families, can give you information about local nursing homes and other available types of housing for the elderly.

❖ **The local hospital's discharge planner or social services department** is responsible for placing patients in rehabilitation centers, nursing homes, assisted living, or other housing situations and therefore knows a great deal about services in your parent's community. Many hospital social workers will guide you whether or not your parent is in the hospital.

❖ **The National Association of Professional Geriatric Care Managers** (520-881-8008) provides referrals to local geriatric care managers who can oversee your parent's care when you can't. Care managers' services are not inexpensive, but they are often well worth the price.

care agency or the state long-term-care ombudsman's office, any of which may be able to send someone over periodically.

◆ Buy your parent a medical alert system so if she becomes ill suddenly or falls when she is alone, she will be able to get help immediately.

◆ Leave a duplicate of your parent's house key with a trusted neighbor or friend, or hide one somewhere outside of her house or apartment in case there is an emergency and someone needs to get in.

◆ Be sure you have a reliable telephone answering machine so your parent or others can reach you in case of an emergency.

◆ Learn about any local elder-watch programs. Some post offices and gas and electric companies train employees to watch for trouble at homes where they know an elderly person lives alone. Sometimes a bank manager will keep an eye out if you are concerned about your parent's finances—is the account suddenly being used up, or has it laid dormant for some time?

♦ From afar, it is especially important to be ready with information and questions when you call doctors or lawyers so you can keep long-distance calls brief. If you are in a different time zone, try to make these calls during off-peak hours.

♦ When things begin to get unwieldy, look into hiring a geriatric care manager or find out if a government agency or charitable group offers free care management. A manager will check on your parent, organize local services for her, handle emergencies and keep you up-to-date.

CARING FOR THE CAREGIVER

Setting Limits • Dealing with Guilt, Anger and Grief
• Achieving a Healthy Mindset

....

WHY WOULD A BOOK ABOUT CARING FOR A PARENT feature a chapter on caring for yourself? Because it's probably the one thing you'll fail to do and it may be the most important thing you can do—both for yourself *and* for your parent.

Don't flip past this chapter too quickly, thinking, *My mother needs me. I don't have time for myself right now.* Your parent's care can easily consume an ever-expanding part of your life. It may begin with a few calls here, some visits there, questions for doctors and lawyers. Then, more visits. More worrying. More phone calls. Before you know it—and sometimes without your even realizing it—you are too busy for friends, distant from your spouse, distracted at work and constantly trying to shake a cold.

You need to use all the help that is available, decide how much you are able to give and then accept that there are limits to what you or anyone else can do in this situation. Gain some perspective, pace yourself and curb your instinct to want to "fix" everything.

You need to take care of yourself, find ways to get away from it all, even to enjoy yourself, in the midst of this ongoing crisis.

Setting Limits

If there were such a thing as Caregivers Anonymous, the first step in the program would be to get rid of that little voice inside you that says, *I can do it all, I am responsible for everything, and whatever I do, it's never enough.*

Of course you want to make your parent well, make her happy, make her safe. In fact, if it were possible for you to be with her every minute of the day, perhaps you would be. But the truth is that you can't personally do everything that needs to be done for her, and trying to do so will only exhaust and frustrate you without really helping your parent over the long haul.

So how do you use your energies most effectively? If your mother has a sudden and severe illness, of course you'll want to be there. But when her needs are more chronic, when you find yourself taking on

> **"***For a long time I visited my mother twice a week, but I was always running and always tired. I started to dread each visit and I was angry at her because I felt it was all her fault. She was ruining my life.***
>
> ***Then a friend said to me, 'This isn't her fault. It's your fault.' And, you know, she was right.***"**
>
> —FRAN M.

more and more responsibility over a matter of months or years, you must step back, take a realistic look at the situation and draw some boundaries for yourself. Determine what you can reasonably do for your parent and, more important, what you have to stop trying to do. As hard as this is, you may be surprised to discover that setting some limits will relieve your guilt and ease some tension. And you will have more patience and energy for those things that only you can give.

◆ **Examine your motivation.** Why are you helping your parent? It sounds like an odd question, but it's a healthy one to mull over. Do you view your parent's care as a burden that was dumped upon you? Do you feel that you have a duty to care for her? *She's my mother, after all!* Or are you helping because, given your parent's situation, this is what you choose to do?

If you are helping your parent hoping to get the praise, respect or love you never had before, you're headed for disappointment. This relationship isn't going to change now. If you are trying to repay your parent for all she did during your childhood, you can't. It's not possible. In fact, it's not a debt anyone ever intended for you to repay.

Take a moment to consider your motivation, think over your options and make a conscious choice about your involvement in your parent's care. Then, accept this as your choice, not as something your parent or an unfair world has imposed upon you. The work you do for your parent will still be difficult, but it will feel more like an interruption and less like an imposition. It will be about love, not about debt.

♦ **Accept and enlist help.** One way to limit what you do is to let others help. And you need to get them involved as soon as possible. If your father needs some assistance around the house, encourage siblings and other relatives to pitch in. If a friend or neighbor offers to lend a hand, say yes. Other people not only can help, but they often want to help. Let them.

Siblings, in particular, should be called on right away. They might have different ideas about your father's care or ways of doing things you might not agree with, but they too have a right to care for him, and besides, he needs them now. You need them, too. If you begin this as a family effort when the tasks are smaller, you will have each other further down the road when the needs and responsibilities tend to be more monumental.

If you don't have siblings or your siblings can't or won't help for some reason, draw on neighbors, aunts, uncles and cousins, local volunteers, and your parent's healthier friends. When more help is needed, consider meal delivery, housekeeping, adult day care and other local services. (Some of these services are free or inexpensive; a few are covered by insurance and Medicaid.) It's important to get hooked up with

> **"**I used to spend hours trying to convince my parents to move out of their big house and to organize their finances. But they didn't do anything. They would ask me questions and listen and act like they were going to do something about it. But they never did.
>
> And then I realized, they are not going to change. They are not going to move until something forces them to. And there is nothing I can do about it. It was terribly difficult to back off. You want so much to help and you know things are only going to get worse. It took me three years to give up and let go, and I still struggle with it sometimes. I just have to go along and see what happens next.**"** —DIANE P.

such supports early because it gives your parent time to get used to them when he is relatively well, and it makes him less dependent upon a sole caregiver—you.

Let other people give *you* a hand as well—pick up your dog at the vet, bring over a casserole, water your plants or stay with your parent on occasion so you can get some rest.

♦ **Let go of futile efforts.** Don't waste precious energy trying to get your parent to change her ways if it's clear that she won't. Tell your mother what you think, get others to help in the effort, but if she still refuses to heed your advice, you have no choice but to give up. For example, if you are spending a lot of time researching group homes for the elderly, and she has absolutely no intention of moving, stop the hunt and move on to more productive tasks (like safeguarding the house that she's in).

You may feel that you have failed. You haven't. You may leave your mother in a risky situation. She may fall or run out of money. But you have done all you can and you cannot do anything more. You can't blame yourself if your parent's refusal to accept help leads to an illness or injury.

Letting go of hopeless crusades is an enormous accomplishment. It enables you and your parent to live within the current situation until events provide a new perspective.

◆ **Rein yourself in.** Be candid with yourself in determining what help is essential. Day-to-day your parent's care may seem more pressing than other matters in your life—*everything* you do for your parent at this point may seem essential—but think about it. Visiting your mother every day may be valuable for both of you, but wouldn't she be okay with fewer visits? Try to distinguish between your impulse to relieve your own anxiety about your parent's welfare and the true demands of the situation.

As you decide what's truly necessary, consider what you may be ignoring or giving up because of the burden of your parent's care. Are you willing to jeopardize your own health? Neglect your children? Damage your career? You may decide to skip a trip to Florida because your father is in the hospital, but when he is in the midst of a prolonged illness, should you cancel a special dinner out with your husband or miss a deadline at work?

Now create a pared-down schedule for yourself that meets your parent's most pressing needs—the things that only you can do for her—while still respecting your own needs. Even if you live with your parent, set some parameters—what hours you will be with her each day, which tasks you will do for her. Schedule time away from her just for yourself.

Be conservative in your plan; it always feels better to increase your commitment than to decrease it. Don't promise to make three visits a week or three visits a month if that puts you over the edge; keep it at two. Then, when you talk with your parent, focus on what you will do for her, not on what you won't.

One quick word of warning: Don't use no-mate-no-kids as an

"When I retired, I didn't tell my mother. I didn't want her to think I was more available, that I had more time for her. I had been taking care of her for several years and when I retired I realized there was a lot that I wanted to do for myself, a lot that I had neglected because of her.

I told her that I was working from home more, in case she called and found me there, but I didn't tell her that I had retired. And I have never regretted it." —BARBARA F.

excuse for doing more than you can reasonably manage or tolerate. Your time is no more expendable, no less important, because you are single. You have a career, relationships and other commitments that need your attention. Don't underrate yourself or your needs, or let a family member make judgments about when you "should" be available.

◆ **Learn to say "no."** Caregivers are often as bad at saying "no" to requests for help as they are at saying "yes" to offers of help. Learn to say no to your parent, certainly, but also learn to say no to yourself. It may be your own psyche and your own needs that drive you to do more than you can handle, while your parent may be fine with less help, with assistance from a community service and with fewer visits.

Women, in particular, often have trouble saying no; they feel they must be the "good girl" or "strong daughter." This martyr syndrome is neither helpful nor "good."

Convince yourself that saying no to certain things is not only okay, but necessary. Practice. Try it out on the dog. Say "no" to the mirror. But get the word out. Confronted with a parent's escalating needs, you may learn, perhaps for the first time in your life, how to act on your own behalf.

◆ **Stick to your guns.** Sure, you can decide to cut back on some visits, even put a plan in writing, but how do you stick to it? Say you decide that your marriage or some other primary relationship needs more attention, but just as you and your mate settle in for a quiet evening together, the first in weeks, you find yourself wondering if your father is all right and feeling guilty for not being with him. You're short with your mate when he asks what's troubling you, or you call your father and feel even worse when he asks why you don't come see him.

Be firm in your resolve. If you decide that you are not going to concern yourself with your father's financial affairs anymore, don't spend an evening researching home equity loans. If you've told your mother you cannot be interrupted during work and she continues to call, remind her quickly and gently that this is not the time to talk and that you'll call her when you get home.

And don't be unduly influenced by how someone else is handling a comparable situation. Just because a colleague sees her mother every weekend and once during the week doesn't mean that you should further strain your schedule. Just because your cousin cared for her mother at home for twelve years and is critical that you aren't doing the same, don't feel apologetic. Only you can create the right balance for yourself. Find it and keep to it.

> **❝***The last time I went to my support group, this woman was talking about her father, who has dementia. She was taking care of him twenty-four hours a day, and she was so warm and had such a nice sense of humor about it all that I thought, 'This woman is a saint.' It made me feel terrible.*❞ —LINDA K.

Emotional Minefields

Taking care of yourself, simply surviving parentcare, requires that you deal with some potent emotions. Believe it or not, reactions you are experiencing now, even the ones that seem disturbingly out of character for you, illogical or childish, are normal and quite common. And most of them can be tempered once you recognize what it is you are feeling and why.

GUILT AND HELPLESSNESS

These are the constant companions of caregivers, with women more often plagued by guilt and men more often frustrated by feelings of helplessness. Women seem to have inherited a burden of guilt from their mothers, and their grandmothers before them. *I'm not doing enough, I'm not doing it right, I should have done something else.* Men, on the other hand, tend to want to fix problems, and become exasperated when they can't be fixed. In general, they also aren't as experienced as women in the hands-on care and empathy that is required when a parent is frail or sick, so they feel all the more helpless. And whatever your gender, distance can compound feelings of guilt and helplessness.

Getting a grip on these emotions is essential, and you'll have to do so again and again, for they have a habit of reappearing. Consider for a moment whatever it is that you think you should be doing for your parent and are not. How reasonable are your expectations? Can you realistically do these tasks? Would performing them help your parent significantly?

Now look at the situation from the opposite perspective. Instead of berating yourself for not doing something, focus on what you *are* doing for your parent. Make a list of these things and be sure to include absolutely everything that

> **"**I wish I was there with my father. Absolutely. I saw him a lot over the summer and that really made me happy. I loved being there for him. But I guess that's easy for me to say from a distance. While I feel a bit at a loss, the grind of being there on a daily basis is very hard on my brother. Because I'm far away, I appreciate each visit, each minute. I am always afraid when I leave that it might be the last time.**"** —JANE C.

you provide—emotional support, regular phone calls, visits, letters, talks with doctors, help with financial matters, assurance that your parent will be cared for in the future and that his wishes will be respected. Recognize and be proud of what you are giving and give it generously.

ANGER AND RESENTMENT

Try to alleviate any anger or resentment as soon as you recognize that you are feeling it.

THOSE UNTHINKABLE THOUGHTS

Many people caring for an aged parent wish, at some point along the way, that this parent would die. It may be a fleeting thought or a constant presence. Either way, it's very disturbing.

If you are wishing your mother would die because she is terminally ill and in pain, then you shouldn't have any guilt about such thoughts. They are normal and, in most cases, even merciful.

The trouble comes when you are wishing your father would die because he has become a burden to you, or because caring for him is using up all the family money, or because you are simply tired of worrying and wondering. In other words, you want him to die less for his sake than for yours. This is a common and natural reaction, but it is jolting when the thought first comes into your mind, and it can produce a great deal of guilt and shame. *I can't believe I'm thinking such things. I must be a really horrible person.*

Watching and caring for an ill parent over time is draining—emotionally, physically and financially. Since there is really no other possible outcome, it is natural to want the struggle to end, for everybody's sake. You are not a bad person for feeling this way. You are only human.

Reframe your resentment. That is, rather than wishing that the person or the situation you're resenting would change, think about what you can do to change things. If you resent your parent because you are doing too much and missing out on your own life, then back off. Do less. If you resent your spouse for not sympathizing or helping, try to understand his perspective and then talk to him about what *you* might do to remedy any conflict.

Anger is more difficult to deal with because it is so hot and blinding. Be careful. Anger can lead to rash acts and regrettable words. When you feel angry, try not to take any action right away. Distance yourself from the situation and wait until you simmer down. Once you're calmer, address the reason for your feelings. You don't want your anger to explode, but you also don't want to suppress it or it will implode.

Ask yourself what made you so stomping mad. What would ease the fury? Can the enraging situation be changed? If not, how can you respond to it differently so you don't become quite so angry the next time?

If you have trouble thinking clearly about this, try writing it down. Writing can help blow off

AROUND AND AROUND WE GO

Don't fall into the anger-guilt-anger cycle. *My mother annoys me. I get angry with her. I feel guilty for getting angry. I resent her for making me feel bad, so I find her even more annoying. Then I get angry....* Recognize the cycle, determine what gets you on this merry-go-round, and then next time, try to stop it before it starts. If you do get angry, forgive yourself immediately. Don't feel guilty. Snapping at your parent and other emotional outbursts are typical reactions to this kind of stress.

a little steam without burning anyone in the process. It can also, with time, help to clarify some issues—and sometimes, as a result, lead to solutions.

Keep a diary for several months, or just let loose on any handy piece of paper whenever you find yourself on emotional overload. If you are uncomfortable addressing a diary, write a letter to the person who caused the anger, a friend, or some made-up therapist, describing the problems and your feelings (but don't send it). While you write, don't think about sentence structure or grammar or legibility, just scribble down the thoughts as they come to you—they will come fast once you let it happen. If it's easier, talk into a tape recorder that you keep by the bed or take along in the car.

If anger or the situation that is precipitating it get beyond your control, talk to a therapist. Therapy can be enormously helpful in sorting out overwhelming feelings of anger.

SORROW AND GRIEF

All of us grieve in our own way, at our own pace. The sadness can be constant, or it may crash over you in waves at odd times. Go with it and allow yourself time to grieve. There is nothing weak or selfish about grieving. And holding in the feelings may make you tense or withdrawn from your parent, when it's the opposite you want. Take some time away from work. Spend time alone if you feel the need, or share your pain with others. Then, while

“My mother has always been my best friend, and after my father died we only became closer. The idea of losing her is too painful for me to bear. She has always been there for me, always understood me. When she is gone, no one will do that for me. I can't imagine my world without her.

Sometimes after I hang up the phone when she sounds down or weak, I feel helpless and sad. I cry so hard that I can't breathe. I guess I'm lucky to have a mother that I love this much, but sometimes I think that if I didn't, it wouldn't hurt so much. ” —CAROL P.

you still have time, let your mother know that you are sad, that you love her, that you will miss her. Don't miss this opportunity to tell her how you feel.

SUPPORT GROUPS

More than anything else, support or self-help groups help you to see that your situation is not unique, that others face many of the same difficult issues and turbulent feelings. This in itself can be an enormous relief. Because group members are usually strangers, it's a safe arena in which to air intimate problems, vent anger or talk about feelings you might be ashamed of. And because you all

"Sometimes in the evening I reach a point when I think, 'I'd just rather not go out tonight.' But I always come home from the support group feeling better. Because everyone in the group is dealing with someone with dementia, it helps me see that what my mom is doing is perfectly normal for this disease. I also see that what I'm feeling isn't cruel or selfish or crazy. Even if I never see these people again when this is over, I'll never forget them." –BARBARA F.

face similar situations, you understand each other in a way that others, even best friends, cannot.

Support groups are particularly

DEEP IN DEPRESSION

Depression is a physical illness that needs immediate medical attention. If you have symptoms of depression—feelings of extreme sadness, relentless waves of self-criticism, apathy and hopelessness, changes in eating or sleeping habits, trouble concentrating, thoughts about death—consult a doctor immediately. Depression can usually be treated quite effectively with counseling and/or medication.

For immediate help call the local crisis intervention, suicide or depression hotline, or 911.

For information about depression and a referral to a local specialist, contact:

The National Foundation for Depressive Illness (800-248-4381)

The National Mental Health Association (800-969-6642)

The National Institute of Mental Health's Depression Awareness, Recognition and Treatment (DART) Program (800-421-4211)

wonderful for people who feel isolated, either because they have no other friends in the same situation or because they aren't interested in opening up to friends or siblings about the subject. Such groups are also a godsend for people who simply feel overwhelmed by their situation and want to see how others handle it (or fail to handle it).

The nature of support groups varies widely in terms of purpose and membership, and you may need to try two or three before finding one that meets your needs. Some groups are designed for people caring for a sick parent, while others zero in on specific issues—family relationships, Alzheimer's, stroke, cancer, death. Some are set up so people can share practical information and resources for help, while others function purely as emotional outlets. Some have leaders, others are group-led. Although support groups are usually for the caregiver, some encourage the parent to attend as well.

To find a support group, call your area agency on aging, Children of Aging Parents (215-945-6900) or the National Self-Help Clearinghouse (212-354-8525). Most nursing homes, adult day-care centers and mental health clinics should also be able to refer you to nearby support groups. If you are interested in a specific topic, look in the phone book for the appropriate association, many of which either run support groups themselves or can refer you to one (for example, the Alzheimer's Association, the American Cancer Society, Emotions Anonymous).

12 Steps to a Healthy Mindset

Setting limits and coping with guilt take a lot of discipline and practice. Here are some more modest and perhaps enjoyable ways to ease stress and take care of yourself. Think of it as your own 12-Step Caregiver Program.

TAKE FIVE

If you are caring for your parent on a regular basis, especially if you are living with him, remove yourself completely from the situation once in a while. You need to refuel and you can't do it without some distance. Do it before you are too distraught to plan or enjoy such a break.

Make arrangements for any necessary fill-in help (a schedule of family, friends, volunteers, home-care workers), or get your parent into one of the many respite programs available at a hospital or nursing home.

Then, while you are away, be completely away. Do something just for yourself. Think about something else. Talk about anything else. Clear your head.

A FRIEND INDEED

When you are caring for an aging parent, quite often the first thing that goes is your social life. Invitations are turned down and friendships are put on hold because you simply do not have the time or the energy for them. If you are living with your parent, social isolation can become a serious problem.

But friends are more important now than ever. They can provide a sympathetic ear, make you laugh, get you thinking about other things and remind you that you are not alone. Studies show that caregivers who have social supports, and use them, experience less depression and illness and generally are less overwhelmed by their responsibilities than those who don't. So rather than cutting yourself off, reach out to your friends. Find a way. Make it a priority. Go out for lunch with them, go for a walk or at least call them on the phone. Just as you would be there for them, your friends want to be there for you.

SHIFT GEARS

Whenever you are feeling Type A, think Type B. Researchers have actually timed people who run through red lights and blast their horns at pedestrians, and they have found that these racers don't save themselves any time at all. In fact, hurrying often slows things down because in the rush you are more apt to spill food on your shirt or misplace your car keys.

Slow down. If you are driving somewhere and it takes twenty minutes to get there, don't try to make it in nineteen. Leave extra time and then relax and use that time to listen to your favorite music or a book-on-tape, or to think about an issue that needs some solitary meditation.

Or simply relish the silence. Stay in the slow lane, wait until the light turns green and leave the honking to the geese.

THE WORRY HOUR

Caring for a parent means worrying—lots and lots of worrying, most of it useless, but nonetheless unavoidable. Rather than stewing during a meeting at work or lying awake at three o'clock in the morning, set aside a specific time, 15 minutes or half an hour each day, just for worrying. It sounds ridiculous, but it works. When you can't stop fretting, jot down whatever it is you are thinking about and know that you will contemplate it during your "worry hour." Then, go back to sleep.

LOVE TO LAUGH

Laughter is a forgotten healer. It makes the world sane (or at least it makes the insanity more fun) and

"My mother had a mastectomy and sometimes she forgets to put her prosthesis in. She'll come downstairs with her shirt all askew and sagging and, after standing there for a minute or two, she'll say, 'Something is not right.'

And I look at her and I have to laugh. 'Mom,' I say, 'you forgot your boob.' And we'll both laugh. She thinks it's funny, too. It could happen to anyone. If we didn't laugh, we would cry. It's that sort of thing."
—CAROL G.

HEALTHY BODY, HEALTHY MIND

The mind-body connection works in two directions. You can boost your physical health with a positive outlook, but you can also improve your outlook by tending to your physical health. Now, when your energy and optimism may be taking a bit of a beating, it is more important than ever that you eat well, exercise and get plenty of rest. Yes, you've heard it all before, but now give it a real try. Make a concerted effort for two or three months to take care of your body, and see if you don't notice a dramatic difference in your mood and attitude.

Good Eating

Good eating habits take up very little extra time, if you follow a few general guidelines.

❖ Don't eat on the run, wolfing down a sandwich in the car or eating stew out of a pot while you talk on the phone. Make meals a time for enjoyment, dinner in particular. Slow down, and even if you are eating alone, set the table, light some candles and put the stew in a dish. Savor the meal.

❖ Plan the week's meals in advance and make a detailed shopping list so you don't have to run to the store for forgotten items or rely on take-out food every night.

❖ Keep your cupboard shelves and freezer packed with good, healthful food (pasta, canned tomatoes, tuna, frozen vegetables, etc.) so there is always something for dinner.

❖ When you cook, make plenty. Freeze extra portions for another day, or turn leftovers into new meals. A large roasted chicken can be used for sandwiches, a chicken omelette, cream of chicken on rice, and then soup.

❖ When buying prepared foods, look for ones with the least amount of fat and sodium.

❖ Make better choices, even when you're in a hurry. Rather than racing out the door in the morning with a cup of coffee and a muffin (most muffins are full of fat), have a hunk of dark, grainy bread and a glass of orange juice. Rather than getting a quick burger at the lunch wagon, opt for a salad or bring your own healthful meal to work.

A Little Sweat

There is nothing like a workout to shed pent-up emotions, clear a muddled head and revive a tired body.

❖ Make it doable. Weight training and rigorous workouts are great for you, but if you hate that sort of thing, find something else. It's better to walk two miles a few times a week and stick to it than to run four miles daily and give up after three weeks. Whatever exercise regime you choose, try to find one that lasts at least 20 minutes and includes some variation.

❖ Make it social. If you find an exercise partner, you will be less apt to excuse yourself from the routine, and you get the added benefit of socializing while you sweat.

❖ Make it useful. If you don't think you have time for exercise, combine errands and physical activity. Rake the yard, walk to work, or clean out the basement. Read the newspaper while you ride on a stationary bike. Talk to a co-worker about a new project while you walk along a track. Or chat with your parent while you stretch.

❖ Make it fun. Exercise doesn't have to be boring. Play tennis, go swimming, skate on a frozen pond, or dance to your favorite Motown songs.

Regular Check-ups

Are you urging your parent to see a doctor but neglecting your own health? Stop postponing that physical or your appointment with the dentist. Don't put off your mammogram or your eye exam any longer. Your parent may provide a handy excuse for you to cancel medical check-ups, but don't.

Zzzzzs

In studies of laboratory rats, scientists have found that severe sleep deprivation is always fatal. In humans, it certainly feels deadly, causing irritability, poor concentration, lack of coordination and forgetfulness. Make rest a priority—go to bed early and take time out for naps when necessary—because it enhances far more than your physical appearance; it bolsters your immune system and keeps your mind clear, alert and calm.

Some Pitfalls

For people under stress, one cup of coffee each morning can gradually turn into three. A glass of wine with dinner can become a scotch before dinner and half a bottle of wine during the meal. Be aware of how much caffeine and alcohol you are consuming because without realizing it you can start imbibing more and more. Avoid using drugs of any kind, including sedatives, antidepressants and antianxiety pills, unless you are taking them under the supervision of a doctor. And be careful not to use food to calm your frazzled nerves. When you reach the bottom of the Pepperidge Farm bag, you won't feel any better; in fact you'll probably feel a little sick.

MAINTAINING A SOCIAL LIFE

If you and your parent live together, you can still have a social life. You just have to be a little flexible.

❖ Leave your parent at home and get a sitter or companion to stay with her, rather than skipping a night out or dragging her into a social situation that will be tiring for her. Even though it may seem like an extravagance *(I don't really have to go out tonight)*, make yourself do it. It's a worthwhile investment in your mental health.

❖ If you want your parent to be involved in a social event, have the guests come to your house rather than going out. Home is a more familiar and comfortable setting for your parent. It also means she can leave the room when she needs to rest, without breaking up the party.

❖ Have a pot-luck supper, with each guest bringing a course, so you're not cooking everything yourself. (If it's a casual gathering, you can ask guests to help prepare and clean up, too.) If you don't feel comfortable having a pot-luck party, at least ask guests to bring wine or dessert to ease some of the workload and expense.

❖ If you decide to cook dinner for guests yourself, make something that's easy to prepare in advance like lasagna or stew, put something on the grill, buy prepared food or order out. And while they are not great for the environment, paper and plastic make for much easier clean-up.

it also makes the body healthier. Scientists have found that a good dose of humor strengthens the immune system, improves circulation, relieves stress and bolsters the spirit.

Of course howling with laughter when someone you love is ill can feel like some sort of sacrilege. You may think that you have to be serious and solemn to reflect the severity of the situation and to show respect for your parent. But you don't. You really don't. It's okay to laugh, no matter how sick or incompetent your parent may be. In fact, the worse things get, the more aggressively you should seek out things to laugh about.

Find something funny about the situation and your parent probably will, too. (Dentures are funny. Certain sourpuss hospital personnel are funny. The Jell-O served in nursing homes is funny, especially if you jiggle it.) See a slapstick movie, visit a goofy friend, scan the comics, play a joke on someone, read a Dave Barry or Molly Ivins book, clown around with your sisters. Whenever you are exhausted and depressed, find some way to laugh—a long, side-splitting, teary, wet-your-pants kind of laugh. It's good medicine.

GET SOME PERSPECTIVE

Take time to read the morning paper or listen to the news. Stay abreast of what's happening in the world, in your community and with your friends. It will help put your problems into perspective and get your mind off your situation.

Likewise, if your parent's illness and needs are a major topic of conversation in your house, or the only topic, plan a meal during which you agree they will not be discussed. Talk about the school play, world events, or just gossip. Do whatever it takes to get away from the subject from time to time.

TAKE ACTION

Anyone caring for a parent is bound to have disagreements with professionals, disputes with institutions and arguments with relatives. Don't just complain to your friends about a chronically late home-care worker, a rude orderly or a poorly run meal service. Talk to the person involved, and if he's not responsive, speak to a supervisor. Take action. Without being belligerent, move up the ranks until you get an acceptable response. Be pleasant but persistent.

Also, get informed. Ask questions when dealing with profes-

sionals. Learn about your parent's ailments, ways to appeal Medicare decisions and patients' rights within a nursing home. Be an educated advocate for yourself and your parent, and don't be afraid to speak up when necessary. It's better than letting problems fester and it often leads to solutions.

AVOID THE COULDA-SHOULDA-WOULDAS

Also known as the If-onlys or the More-better-different syndrome, it's a dangerous mindset: *I should have . . . If only . . .* ad infinitum.

Wishing for things that can't be, regretting what is, or daydreaming about how things used to be is futile and potentially destructive if it keeps you from more productive tasks. It's human nature to think this way, but try not to focus on what might have been, and look instead at what is and what can be.

PURSUE OTHER INTERESTS

Hobbies, sports and other such pursuits are not frivolous pastimes. Clearing your mind of your worries —even for brief interludes—will allow you to regain balance and energy. So don't forgo your pottery, gardening, tennis or oil painting, or feel guilty about enjoying them. Make it a point to find time for them. Take pleasure in them.

SPIRITUAL SUPPORT

Whether you are religious or not, spiritual issues often arise when

"*During my father's illness I got very depressed and closed in. I realized that I needed some outlet, some way of dealing with the constant anxiety or else I was going to become a basket case. I don't have a lot of friends and I didn't particularly feel like spending time with those I do have. So I started drawing.*

I hadn't done any sketches since I was a little girl, but I bought a pad and some pens and began sketching. It's my escape now. For some reason, I can express my rage and fear in drawings better than I can with words. I sketch each night after supper, and I look forward to it all day. It's my sanity. I've actually gotten pretty good at it." —ELEANOR R.

a parent is sick, for the situation provokes troubling questions: *Why would a loving God do this? How do I ease my anguish or grief? How do I face my own mortality?* A little guidance may help strengthen your will and focus your life.

If going to religious services doesn't interest you, or if you simply want a more personal discussion, most clergy are happy to meet with people individually. Just call. (You can send a little donation if you want to repay the favor.) Sometimes friends can provide spiritual support, even if they just sit quietly with you and listen.

MEDITATION, MASSAGE AND RELAXANTS

You don't know how much stress you are carrying around until you sit in a relaxation class and let go of it. The techniques you learn there can be used anywhere, anytime, to ease the pressure. Classes in tai chi, meditation and yoga, as well as in general relaxation, all relieve stress. To find out about them, call local gyms, spas, and recreation centers or check the bulletin board at a local health-food store.

If you can afford it, give yourself a real treat by having a massage. You can get the name of a good masseuse or masseur from a doctor or physical therapist or sports medicine center, or by calling the American Massage Therapy Association (847-864-0123).

INDULGENT NECESSITIES

It may sound like an oxymoron, but some indulgence is a necessity. Everyone needs some pampering occasionally, for both physical and mental health. So treat yourself to a long, hot bath, a shopping spree, an exquisite dinner, room service in a hotel, a facial, an afternoon in the sun, a morning lounging in bed, a new hair style—whatever brings you that special, mischievous pleasure that comes only from indulging yourself.

TIPS FOR DAILY LIVING

An Ounce of Prevention • Safe-proofing the Home
• Hygiene • Eating • The Question of Driving
• Exercising Body and Mind

....

WHO CAN HELP BUT WORRY ABOUT AN ELDERLY parent getting through the day, or even part of the day, alone? *What if Dad doesn't bother to eat dinner on his own? I wish Mother would stop driving.* And yet, nearly 1.5 million people over the age of 85 live alone (nearly 10 million people over 65 live alone) and millions of others spend at least part of the day on their own.

If your father has arthritis, fuzzy vision, or some residual paralysis from a stroke, it doesn't mean that it's time for a nursing home or that you have to follow him around tending to his every need. You don't want to do it and he probably doesn't want you to, either. What you can do is help him rearrange his house and revise his habits so that he can live as independently as possible.

Ask your parent about the details of his day or spend a day with him observing how he goes about his basic chores. Does he have trouble holding his razor, walking down stairs, heating up spaghetti or locking the door? Does he have a way to get groceries or visit a friend? Once you know the day's snags, brainstorm solutions with your parent. (Be sure to involve him.) There are a number of ways to make cooking more manageable, dressing more doable, exercise more feasible and free time more entertaining. If you need help with a specific problem and don't find a solution here, contact an occupational therapist, visiting nurse, carpenter or electrician, depending upon the situation.

Safety First

Bad eyesight, dull hearing, arthritis, poor balance, multiple medications, illness and other health problems all put your parent at risk for accidents. Look through her house for hazards. Be particularly thorough if your parent suffers from any sort of confusion.

◆ Make sure that chemicals, harsh cleaners, insecticides, medications, paints, etc. are all labeled with big, clear letters. If your parent gets confused easily, put them out of sight completely.

◆ Check to see that smoke detectors work. Your parent's waning sense of smell makes a smoke detector that much more important.

◆ Check for easy escape routes in case of fire. Your parent won't be able to climb out of a window as easily as you can, so look for escapes she could use. Is the back door wide enough for your mother's wheelchair? Is there a back stairway that your father can manage? If possible, hold a fire drill. If your bedridden parent wouldn't be able to escape, call the local fire department and ask for safety instructions.

◆ Buy a small fire extinguisher that is easy to handle and put it in a convenient place, preferably near the kitchen, where fires may start. And instruct your parent in how to use it.

◆ Have at least two flashlights, with working batteries, ready to use and easy to find if the lights go out. Put one by your parent's bed and one on a kitchen table. If there is a blackout, several large flashlights are safer than candles.

◆ Make sure all bathroom and kitchen outlets contain working circuit interrupters to prevent shocks.

◆ In the kitchen, check to see that the burners and the oven work properly. Be sure that outlets are not overloaded, and that wires don't rest on a hot toaster, for example. Is your mother apt to reach for equipment located above the hot stove, in which case a sleeve or apron string might catch fire? If so, rearrange things.

◆ Because of their thinner skin and slower reactions, elderly people are at risk for scalding. Set the hot water heater so the temperature of the water doesn't rise above 120°F.

◆ If your parent gets cold easily, buy him some good long underwear and turn up the heat. Be careful with space heaters and electric blankets, as they can cause burns and fires.

♦ Keep a list of clearly written, large-print emergency phone numbers by *every* phone, or program them into the telephone's memory. The list should include police, fire, ambulance, your home and work numbers and the phone number of a nearby relative or neighbor. Don't assume your parent will remember your number, or even 911, if she's injured, burglarized or in some other trouble. Even the keenest minds can go blank during moments of panic.

MEDICAL EMERGENCY IDENTIFICATION

Slip a medical identification card into your parent's wallet so in case there is ever an emergency, medical crews will know who he is, whom to contact and whether there are any medical conditions (dementia, diabetes, heart disease, allergies) that require special attention.

You can make one yourself or, in many locations, the area agency on aging distributes free identification tags which either hang on a chain or are placed in a wallet. Otherwise, some companies sell them (look under "Medical Emergency Information" in the Yellow Pages).

MEDICAL ALERT SYSTEMS

"I've fallen and I can't get up" made for a funny ad, but the message was quite serious. Medical alert systems (or emergency response systems) are worth the investment if you are worried about your parent living alone. (Installing one makes a nice gift that says, "I care.")

With these devices, your parent is given a "help" button about the size of a pendant, which she wears on a necklace or bracelet. When she falls, has chest pains or needs help for any other reason, she pushes the button, which sends a signal to a receiver next to her telephone, which in turn dials a response center (most systems are set up so they can dial out even if the phone is off the hook). At the response center, your parent is identified by a code. The responder calls her house and communicates with her either over the phone or, if she cannot get to the phone, through a two-way intercom attached to the phone. If your parent doesn't respond to the call or says that there is, indeed, an emergency, the responder then calls an emergency crew.

Dozens of companies now sell emergency response systems. You can find them in the Yellow Pages under "Medical Alarms," or check with a medical supply store. Or you can ask your parent's doctor if the hospital he is affiliated with offers such a service. Prices vary, so call several companies. Some sell the system (for anywhere from $200 to $2,000) and then charge a monthly service fee, while others lease systems (for $20 to $50 a month, after an initial installation charge). Renting is usually preferable because you don't have to worry about repairs or the company going defunct or moving.

When comparing systems, ask for details about the staff receiving the emergency calls. Are they situated nearby? How are they trained? Do they speak your parent's native language if it's not English? Find out the company's average response time (if they are not checking their response time periodically, they should be). Ask if your parent can try the system for a trial period or get a money-back guarantee. Be sure your parent can operate the buttons, and then test the system to see how well it operates within his house and how far he can venture into the backyard, for example, before the system fails.

Once your parent has an emergency response system, check the batteries regularly. It's no good to have it if it's not working.

CRIME PREVENTION

The elderly are popular targets for criminals because they are easy prey. But your parent shouldn't lock himself in the house because he is afraid of being mugged. Even if he is physically frail, common sense can protect him from most dangerous situations.

Talk to your parent about the precautions he should take and what he should do in specific situations. Do some role playing. Going through the motions now will mean quicker and smarter reactions should there ever be a problem. Check with the local senior center or police department to find out about talks on crime prevention, or see if a police officer might speak with your parent individually about safety. In the meantime:

◆ Let the local police department know that your parent is elderly and living alone, especially if he lives in a small town where the police might pay some special attention to him.

◆ Make sure your parent can properly operate all his home door locks and that he uses them. Get locks that can be opened from the inside without a key, in case he needs to exit quickly.

◆ Install a peephole in the front door. Your parent should not open the door for anyone unfamiliar—a salesman or repairman—unless he has asked the person to come. He can also invest in an intercom for the front door.

◆ If he doesn't already have one, install a security alarm system in your parent's house. You can also install "panic buttons," which alert the police or security guards to trouble, by his bed or favorite chair.

◆ Several companies now sell remote controls that operate house lights as well as a radio or a television from afar. When your parent arrives home at night, he can light up the house and even make it noisy several minutes before entering, allowing burglars time to escape. You can also install exterior floodlights that can be operated from the bedroom.

◆ Talk with your parent about where and when it is best for him to walk outdoors. There may be certain routes to the store or the park that are safer than others, and particular times of day when he should opt for cabs or buses.

◆ Your parent should leave diamond rings or expensive watches at home when traveling in cities or in any crime-ridden areas. They attract thieves and pickpockets.

♦ Money and credit cards should be carried in an inside pocket or money belt rather than a purse, which can be snatched. Nevertheless, your parent should always carry a little cash ($20 or $30) with him so he has something to hand over to a mugger.

Preventing Falls

Everyone catches a toe or trips on a step occasionally, but now a minor tumble can have major repercussions. Older bodies break more easily than younger ones and they don't heal as quickly or as completely. Then, while they are trying to heal, enforced bed rest exacerbates previous medical ills and can cause new ones, such as pneumonia, infections, bedsores and other circulatory disorders. Half of all older people who fracture a hip end up needing canes, walkers or wheelchairs for the rest of their lives. Twenty-five percent of people entering nursing homes cite falls as the primary reason for the move.

Falls can also make an older person needlessly cautious. After a fracture has healed, even when the fall didn't cause any real injury, your parent may be afraid to move around. Sedentary, he may become dependent, isolated and depressed.

The bottom line: Prevent falls in the first place. Your parent needs good medical care, a safe house and exercise to improve mobility, coordination and strength.

> **❝***My mother rode three miles every day on a stationary bicycle until she was ninety-six years old. She volunteered, she traveled, she read. But when she fell and broke her ankle she was immobile for a couple of months and I think that just killed her spirit. She could never really get around very well after that and her mood, her body, everything just went. She died a year later.***❞** —MEL T.

While everyone with an older parent should be alert to the threat of falls, you need to be particularly cautious if your parent has osteoporosis, Parkinson's disease, dementia, poor eyesight or arthritis, or if your parent has any injury or disability in the legs, has fallen before, has had a stroke or is taking medications that might make him dizzy or faint.

ROOM-BY-ROOM PREVENTION

If you request it, a visiting nurse or an occupational or physical therapist will examine your parent's home for hazards and show you how to reduce risks. If the inspection is done as part of a hospital discharge, Medicare or other insurance policies may cover the cost. But you can also tour your parent's house yourself and look for places where she has to bend, reach, stoop or step over something. Look for anything that might trip her up or get in her way. Here are the most important steps toward preventing a fall:

PRACTICE MAKES PERFECT SENSE

Show your parent what to do in case he falls. If possible, get him to lie down and then roll onto his hands and crawl to a phone or to a piece of furniture that he can use for support while he hikes himself up. Such practice may sound a little silly, but when people fall they often become confused and disoriented. If they have practiced what to do in advance, it will come to them naturally when they need to do it.

Floors and Pathways

• Check carpets for worn areas and rips. Tack down flaps or curled edges.

• Use low-pile, wall-to-wall carpeting wherever possible. Avoid thick-pile carpets.

• Get rid of throw rugs or make sure they have rubber, nonskid backing on them.

• Use nonslip wax or be sure that wax is buffed thoroughly.

• Make sure floors are even and level. Repair loose floorboards and remove thresholds at doorways.

• Clear hallways and other pathways of wastepaper baskets, footstools, magazine racks, electrical wires and other small objects.

• If your parent has any hanging plants, be sure she doesn't have to duck to get past them (or reach up on tiptoes to water them).

• Install handrails in hallways.

Stairs

• Avoid stairs completely, if possible. This may mean turning a downstairs den into a bedroom or building ramps onto short stairways. You can also buy a lift which carries a passenger up and down stairs in a chair—expensive, but helpful if you can afford one.

• When stairs are unavoidable, be sure handrails are sturdy and extend the full length of the stairs. Handrails should be placed on both sides of the stairs. Don't forget stairs leading to a basement and those by the front and back doors.

• Ideally, each step should be no more than six inches high. Taller steps may be cause for concern.

• Mark the edges of steps—or any place the floor changes elevation even slightly—with brightly-colored adhesive tape.

• Use nonslip treads on stairs. Consider getting rid of carpeting on stairways, as it rounds off the edges of steps and shortens the depth of each step, making footing precarious.

Furniture

• Make sure that chairs are high enough to get out of and into easily, and that they have strong armrests and high backs that can be used for support. If necessary, keep a walker or cane by the chair or look into electric-powered pneumatic chairs that lift a person up and lower him down.

• Likewise, make sure the bed is not too high or too low, so your parent can get in and out easily.

• Get rid of beds and other furniture with nonlocking wheels.

• Furniture legs that curve outward create a tripping hazard. Move such furniture out of any pathway or get rid of it.

• Avoid tripod tables which are not sturdy.

• Repair broken or wobbly furniture immediately.

Bathrooms and Kitchens

• Install grab bars near toilets and tubs, and get a raised toilet seat, which makes sitting and standing far easier.

• Attach a wall-mounted, liquid soap dispenser in the shower.

• Install nonslip strips on the floor of the tub or shower.

• Place nonslip strips or rubber-bottom bathmats on the bathroom floor. Keep a nonslip rug or runner, or a rubber mat, in front of the kitchen sink where the floor is apt to be wet and slippery.

• Avoid or be careful when using oils in the bath; they make feet and hands slippery.

• A shower curtain may be easier to manage than a glass door, but make sure it's hung on a secure rod that is screwed into the wall, not a tension rod. If your parent slips, a curtain on a screwed-in rod will offer better support.

• Your parent or someone else in the household should clean up any grease, water or other spills right away.

Lighting

• Lighting should be bright and evenly distributed. Older eyes need more light. They also don't adjust quickly to changes in lighting, so avoid having dark hallways that lead into brightly lit stairways, or vice versa.

• Reduce glare by aiming lights at a

"My father has this little, three-legged pine table in his living room, right by his favorite chair. Every time he got up or sat down, he would lean on the table, using it for balance. I told him a hundred times that the table was wobbly, and that one day he was going to lean on it, fall over and kill himself. I even bought him a new table one year, but he didn't use it. He's pretty stubborn. He said, 'I've had this table here for forty-five years and I haven't fallen yet. Why would I fall now?'

But I think my warning sank in a little, even though he would never admit it. I've noticed that he doesn't really lean on that table anymore. He puts more weight on the chair. He listens if I bother him enough about something. I just have to be a little more stubborn than he is."
—SKIP R.

wall or the ceiling, and use low-glare bulbs and lampshades. If there is a sunny window facing your parent as he uses the stairs, hang curtains or shades to block the glare.

• Install a light by the bed so your parent isn't fumbling around at night when she needs to get up. Make sure light switches are easy to use, easy to reach and accessible at the entrance of each room so your parent isn't walking through a dark room to get to a light.

• Use night-lights in the hallway, the bathroom, the kitchen, the stairway or anywhere else your parent might venture at night.

• You might want to install sound-activated lights which go on when your parent gets up during the night and go off after he has stopped moving around. Look for them in catalogues, medical supply stores, hardware or lighting stores.

Other Measures

• Make sure your parent has comfortable, sturdy, nonslip shoes with low, broad-based heels. Sneakers with splayed soles provide a solid base. Avoid sandals and shoes with open heels or toes. Bedroom slippers should have rubber soles. If your mother likes to walk around in just her socks, get socks with rubber pads on the bottom.

• Teach your parent how to rise from chairs and beds gradually to avoid dizziness. She should get up in stages, with two hands planted firmly on armrests or other supports.

• Make sure the house is warm enough—the thermostat probably needs to be higher than it used to be. Low body temperature can lead to hypothermia and dizziness, which can, in turn, lead to falls.

• Organize things so that frequently used items are within easy reach, to discourage your parent from exerting himself or climbing on chairs.

• Place telephones in those places where your parent spends the most time—next to the bed, by his easy chair—and within easy reach. Or get him a portable phone. (But he has to take it with him and not lose it or it will be more trouble than it's worth.)

• Install grab bars by the closet, so when your parent is dressing he has something to hold onto for balance.

• If it will help his mobility, encourage your parent to use a cane or walker. It should be fitted by a doctor and he should be taught how to use it correctly.

• If your father uses a cane, attach a loose wrist strap to one end. Then, if he drops it, it won't fall to the ground and leave him in the precarious position of having to stoop to pick it up.

• Get your parent to limit her drinking, as alcohol certainly will make her unsteady.

• In winter, your parent should keep a bag of rock salt or sand by the front door, so he can toss a few scoops on icy steps. He needs to beware of wet, slippery or uneven pavement. Tell him to walk on grass or loose snow instead of hard, wet or icy patches, and to step slowly over slippery surfaces, with his feet apart and his knees slightly bent. (And remember those rubber soles!)

IF YOUR PARENT FALLS

If your parent falls and doesn't seem to have broken any bones (no severe pain or difficulty moving), help her up by supporting her and then lifting with your legs, not your back. This means bending at your knees, getting a good hold and pushing up with your legs. Don't twist your body to turn her around; pivot by taking small steps.

If your parent is heavy, you may have to push her, a little bit at a time. Get her to a sturdy table or bring a table or chair to her, so she can lift herself up with your help. Talk to her as you move her, telling her exactly what you are doing. If you cannot get her up, don't pull

MEDICAL ALERT

If your parent has a serious fall and is in pain, don't move her unless you need to restore her breathing or get her away from fire, out of water or clear from some other danger. Call an emergency crew. Cover her with a blanket if it's cool and assure her that medical help is coming. Continue to talk to her in a calm voice until help has arrived.

your own back out trying. Wait for help to arrive.

Whether or not she is injured, have your parent make an appointment with her doctor so he can determine what caused her to fall and can talk to her about ways of preventing accidents in the future. Falls are sometimes indicators that a drug is causing problems or that your parent has an illness such as dehydration, heart disease, stroke, infection, pneumonia or internal bleeding.

Bathing and Grooming

In addition to preventing falls, grab bars in the bathroom and raised toilet seats make life easier for aching knees and backs. Also, lever-style faucets, rather than knobs, are easier to use for arthritic hands. They are a good idea for door and cabinet handles, as well.

Beyond these items, medical supply stores and mail-order catalogues sell a mind-boggling array of bathroom gizmos—some of them more useful than others—including a razor holder that attaches to the hand, a dental floss holder for people who have trouble winding the little thread around their fingers, and a wall-mounted soap dispenser. You can also find sponges with long handles, toothbrushes with thick handles and a variety of nail clippers, toothpaste dispensers, mirrors, shower-head attachments and urinals that are simple to use. Even if you don't buy anything, it's worth flipping through a few cat-

MORE THAN CLEAN—BEAUTIFUL

Good hygiene is important not only for good health (poor hygiene can lead to skin infections), but also for self-esteem. People feel better when they look good. A new hairdo and some makeup may improve your mother's outlook, energy level and, to some extent, even her health. Your father will feel more dapper and proud with a clean shave and combed hair.

Make sure your parent has the proper tools not only for basic hygiene but also for preening and primping. Your father may be able to use the toilet safely but can he clip his nails, shine his shoes and open his after-shave? Can your mother manage a powder puff, a mascara brush or hair curlers? (She may say that she doesn't care about makeup anymore, in an effort to hide her problems. So you have to play sleuth.) If easy-to-open lids and other handy devices don't help, find out about local barbers and beauticians who make house calls. Some offer discounts to senior citizens.

When my mother's hair started to fall out after the chemotherapy, I didn't think much about it. We all knew it would happen, and she's never been terribly concerned about her appearance.

A friend of hers suggested that she buy a wig. I thought, 'Mom? In a wig? Never!' But sure enough, she bought one and she wears it all the time. She looks pretty good in it and it's made a big difference in how she feels. She has a lot more confidence.
—DIANA M.

alogues for ideas about things you can make yourself. For instance, simply wrapping a strip of foam around a toothbrush handle makes it easier to hold.

If you or someone else is helping your parent bathe and brush:

◆ Buy a chair made for the shower or use a regular plastic chair as long as it's stable and won't slip. You can also buy a rubber device that deflates to lower a person gently into the tub and then inflates to get them out again.

◆ If your parent is completely immobile, a sponge bath is as good as a regular bath. Typically a home health aide will bathe your parent, but if you are doing it yourself, prepare a bowl of warm, slightly soapy water and with a soft washcloth wipe her down, top to bottom, being sure to get into all cracks and under every fold of skin. Dry thoroughly. You can also buy a rubber basin for hair-washing in a bed or in a chair, or a full-body tub for the

"In my mother's era you took baths. She never used the shower. Ever. But I couldn't get her into the tub. And if I did, she couldn't get up once she got down. I said to her, 'A shower is so wonderful. You don't know what you're missing.' But she absolutely would not do it.

Finally, she did try it, not long ago. She had her first shower at ninety-some years old. I said, 'Isn't this wonderful?' You know, I'm standing outside and she's in there, but I'm holding her and I'm getting all wet. She wouldn't say that she liked it. But she accepted it."

—MARGARET F.

bed (which may be a little unwieldy).

◆ It is easier to brush someone else's teeth with an electric toothbrush. Use very little toothpaste or avoid it altogether. When your parent is quite sick, simply use a wet, soft toothbrush or damp washcloth or disposable mouth cleaner (available in medical supply stores) to wipe the teeth, gums and tongue.

In the Dressing Room

If your parent has trouble reaching the zipper on the back of her dress or managing the tiny buttons on her sweater, explore the latest line of "easy clothing"—dresses with large zipper handles, pants with Velcro closures, shirts with snaps, shoes that slip on and skirts that pull on. There are also gadgets that make dressing easier, such as metallic arms or "grippers" that help pull socks and pants on and devices that pull buttons through their holes.

But before you order a new specialized wardrobe for your parent, peruse the racks of the department stores or make adjustments to clothing your parent already owns—it will be a lot cheaper and probably more attractive. Buttons can be replaced with zippers or Velcro; elastic shoelaces turn a tie-up shoe into one that slips on; jersey dresses with wide necks slide over the head, and wraparound dresses pull on like a coat. Sweatpants and tops are often the easiest (and most comfortable) outfits to wear, and many stores now sell dressier elastic-waisted pants.

Don't forget the little touches that make your parent feel attractive and proud. Buy a clip-on tie for your father, if he's a tie-wearer with tired fingers. Give your mother a colorful silk scarf, which hides humped shoulders, surrounds the face with color and makes her feel special. (You can tie it permanently so all she has to do is slip it over her head.)

What's for Dinner?

Does your parent skip breakfast, dine on a corner of yesterday's sandwich, or return meal trays that have barely been touched? Is he growing thinner by the day, or maintaining his weight entirely on cookies and chips? If so, it's time to act. A poor diet will worsen his health and deprive him of energy.

Studies suggest that nearly a quarter of the elderly in this country are malnourished—not starving, but failing to get the vitamins, minerals and other nutrients that their bodies need. But the problem is typically overlooked by doctors, who examine heart function and brain waves, not lunch plates, so it's up to you to monitor your parent's eating habits. You can make some simple changes that will vastly improve your parent's meager diet.

IN THE GROCERY STORE

◆ Once a month—on a shopping trip with you or someone else who can help with heavy bags—your parent should stock up on frozen and canned foods, pasta, rice, beans, cereal and other staples that keep well. (Bread, butter, cream and meats can all be frozen and used at a later date.) Interim shopping trips can be used for getting light loads of fresh fruits, vegetables and dairy products.

NOT TOO FAT FOR ME

If there's anything wonderful about old age, it's that thin is not always better. Studies suggest that older people who are a little bit overweight fare better through illness and surgery because they have some extra reserve to call on. So unless your parent has arthritis, osteoporosis, heart disease, diabetes or another condition that requires weight control, she shouldn't worry about a little plumpness.

When the weight should go. If your parent needs to lose weight for health reasons, forget the fad diets, which tend to fail and usually aren't very healthful. Have a doctor or registered dietitian work out a meal plan for her, or use your common sense to teach her more healthful eating habits. She shouldn't aim for a large weight loss. Losing five to ten percent of her weight, a more attainable goal, is enough to lower her blood pressure, reduce her cholesterol levels, improve her diabetes or relieve the pressure on her joints.

When the weight should not have gone. Sudden and unintentional weight loss can signal a number of serious problems, including depression, cancer, heart failure, worsening dementia and malnutrition. If you notice such a weight change, urge your parent to talk with his doctor about it.

◆ Your parent should read the labels, looking for products with the lowest sodium and fat content. (Canned vegetables often contain sodium and syrup or butter sauces; frozen ones are usually a better choice.) Frozen and prepared dinners are more healthful than they used to be and can be supplemented with a salad, steamed vegetables or a piece of fresh fruit.

◆ "Long-life," or UHT, milk (heated at ultra-high temperatures), costs a little more but can be stored on the shelf at room temperature for up to six months. (Once it is opened, it must be refrigerated and lasts about ten days.) It is perfectly safe, quite tasty if chilled before drinking, and just as nutritious as regular milk.

❝In the weeks and months after my father died, my mother didn't eat much. She couldn't be bothered to make a real meal just for herself. She said she hated eating alone. So she lost a lot of weight, which was bad because she was thin to start with.

I taught her how to sauté vegetables in a wok and showed her a few easy pasta and rice recipes—all things she can do in one pot with very little work. Whenever I visit I load up her shelves and refrigerator with food. She protests a lot, but she eats it. Maybe only because she can't stand to see things go to waste.❞

—ALICIA B.

◆ Some dietary supplement drinks, like Ensure, or powdered breakfast drinks are useful on those days when your parent doesn't feel up to cooking or eating.

◆ Buy in small quantities. If your father is shopping for one, he should ask the grocer to break open large containers and give him just two potatoes or a half-dozen eggs. Most stores will do this. He can also buy small portions of cheese, cooked meat, a pint of milk, a half pound of hamburger—so unused food doesn't spoil.

◆ If your mother walks to the corner grocery or has to transport her bags from the bus stop, get her a hand cart for toting them.

◆ If you can't help out with the shopping, find out if a grocery store in her neighborhood delivers, or see if a local volunteer or a friendly neighbor will take her shopping occasionally.

IN THE KITCHEN

◆ Update the kitchen equipment. Small toast-and-broil ovens, microwaves and woks are convenient for single-serving meals, and small food processors are helpful for chopping and slicing.

◆ If your parent uses a gas range, make sure the dials are easy to read. If she has poor vision or suffers from any confusion, mark the "off" position clearly with a strip of colored tape.

◆ If your parent has stiff joints or weak muscles, there are dozens

KEEP IT CLEAN

While most of us can tolerate hundreds of germs without any ill effects, the elderly are more vulnerable to food poisoning and less likely to recover easily once they get it. So take special precautions.

❖ Get your parent to throw out food that is past the expiration date, moldy or smelly. If his sense of smell isn't what it used to be, he should mark foods with a date when he buys it.

❖ Food that is susceptible to bacteria—salads, meats, sauces—should always be refrigerated and never left sitting on the counter. (It's okay to put warm food directly into the freezer.) Thaw frozen foods in the refrigerator or the microwave, not on the counter.

❖ When handling raw meat, especially chicken, your parent should rinse it well and then wash everything it has touched before moving on to the next stage of cooking. Bacteria from the raw chicken can easily travel to the salad if the two are chopped on the same surface, and unwashed hands are common carriers of bacteria.

❖ Cook meat thoroughly. Rare meat is a poor choice for anyone who is frail or elderly.

❖ Wash the kitchen sponge in the dishwasher and throw the dish towel into the washing machine every few days—both gather germs.

❖ Use a wooden cutting board instead of a plastic one; bacteria don't live as well in wood.

Call the Department of Agriculture's Meat and Poultry Hotline (800-535-4555) or the Food and Drug Administration's Seafood Hotline (800-332-4010) for more information about food storage and safety.

---

of aids that can be bought—jar openers, spoon holders, lightweight cookware, stirring devices, etc.—to make cooking easier.

◆ Put lazy Susans in cabinets that are full of small items so your parent has easy access to them.

◆ Move utensils, plates, food, pans and other frequently used items to lower shelves or onto the countertop so your parent doesn't have to reach to high shelves or stoop to get things from low places.

◆ Buy your parent some (large-print, if necessary) cookbooks with easy recipes that serve just one or two people. Some cookbooks cater to special diets, with low-salt or fat-free dishes. Or show your parent how to make a few easy dishes. He can add vegetables, beans, tofu or rice to a can of broth or other soup; toss some tomatoes, cheese, vegetables or left-over meat into a helping of pasta or fold it into a small omelet; or sauté an assortment of favorite foods in a wok.

◆ If you bring food to your parent, make sure that he can easily open and heat whatever you bring. He may just toss it out, not wanting to admit that he couldn't undo the twist-tie on the bag or unwrap the foil.

◆ To perk up food, rather than adding more salt or sugar, your parent should throw in some herbs, spices, extracts, lemon or garlic, and he should heat food whenever possible, so it gives off more aroma. A variety of textures on the plate—crunchy vegetables, creamy sauces, crispy crusts—also makes a meal more appetizing.

◆ If you are cooking for your parent, prepare the foods she prefers. She may be much happier with meat loaf, baked beans and rice pudding than with fancier fare.

AT THE TABLE

◆ Make dining social. Elderly people often fail to eat well purely because they don't like to eat alone. Join your father for meals occasionally, and when you can't be there urge him to get together with friends. He might enjoy a regular potluck dinner, to which each person brings one simple item, or a regular dinner date with a friend.

◆ Make it special. When your mother dines alone, encourage her to put her dinner on a plate, rather than eating it out of the pan, and to sit down at the table to eat. She might also have a glass of wine, if that makes dining more enjoyable.

MEAL PROGRAMS

Congregate meals offered at local community centers, churches and senior centers are nutritious, social and inexpensive (or free). Even if your parent goes only once or twice a week, you'll know that he's eating well at least some of the time. (Some senior centers also provide transportation to meals.) If he can't or won't go out, find out about meal-delivery services, which are also inexpensive or free.

◆ If your parent has trouble handling utensils, buy him forks and knives with longer, heavier, thicker or bent handles; glasses with built-in straws; and plates with rims.

◆ Food that doesn't have to be cut up is easier for less dexterous hands, and finger food is often easier for people with dementia, who can be confused by utensils.

◆ Portions should be small so meals don't look overwhelming. The sheer volume of food may spoil your parent's limited appetite.

AT HOME, IN THE BEDROOM

If your parent is in bed or in a bedroom most or all of the time, you need to set up his room for days of dining and entertainment, as well as safety. If you don't live with your parent, many of these things can be done during a visit.

❖ Make sure your parent is situated on the same floor as a bathroom, preferably close to his room. Otherwise, buy a commode for his room. (Medicare will often cover the cost.)

❖ If you have any choice, select a room for your parent that has a large window and a view, or bright, cheery pictures on the wall.

❖ Arrange the room so there is a sitting area for your parent and for visitors—a chair or two, a reading lamp and a table near a window or in front of a television set, for example.

❖ Place a table near the bed where you can store all the day's needs—magazines or books, pills, a water glass and pitcher, lamp, telephone, radio, writing paper, clock, calendar, remote controls, etc.

❖ Set up a television so your parent can watch it easily, and make sure he has a remote control.

❖ Buy a large pillow for sitting up comfortably in bed (most department stores sell cushions for reclining, and medical supply stores have large triangular-shaped foam cushions for propping people up), and supplement this with lots of regular pillows.

❖ If the house is large, put a bell or a baby monitor by the bed so your parent can call for someone if necessary. Or buy a telephone with an intercom so he can summon help.

❖ Stock some crackers and other nonperishable foods by the bed so you don't have to come running every time your parent wants a snack. You might even buy a miniature refrigerator for his room or load up a cooler with food each morning.

❖ You can buy or rent all sorts of equipment to make bed rest more manageable—for example, an electric or manual hospital bed, side-rails for getting up or turning over; a trapeze above the bed to grab and pull up on; a hospital-style table that slides over the bed; wheelchairs and walkers. These items are expensive, but some may be covered by Medicare.

❖ If your parent is bedridden, you or whoever is caring for her should be on the lookout for bedsores.

◆ When your family dines together, let your parent eat at her own pace. Have her start before the others sit down, or let the children leave the table while she finishes. If she feels that others are waiting for her, she may quit in mid-meal, or worse, hurry and choke on something.

◆ If your parent lives with you, don't enforce "normal" mealtimes. Sometimes, as people grow older, the established routines don't work anymore. Your mother may eat six small meals a day instead of three larger ones. For her nibbling, have healthful snacks on hand, such as chopped vegetables, raisins and other dried fruit, popcorn, cole slaw, yogurt, cheese, humus, meat slices, apples and other fresh fruit, or peanut butter and crackers.

WHEN EATING IS DIFFICULT

If your parent has trouble chewing and swallowing, is confined to bed or unable to feed herself, you or some other caregiver will be more involved in her dining habits.

◆ Anyone who's had a baby knows that most food can be pulverized into a gruesome-looking but healthful mush. A mini food-processor or blender (or even a hand-held masher) will grind meat, mash potatoes and puree vegetables and fruit. Also, try scrambled eggs, oatmeal (banana, cinnamon or raisins add flavor), egg salad, custard, applesauce or flavored gelatin. When you have no time, baby food straight from the jar is soft, nutritious and perfectly good for adults—the fruit selections are actually tasty.

◆ Sauces help dry food slide down more easily, and there is no end to the possibilities—cream, apple, barbecue, gravy, lemon, wine, tomato, cheese. And thicker liquids are easier to swallow than thin ones, especially if your parent is trying to drink while lying in bed.

◆ If you are feeding your parent, never hurry her or thrust oversized bites at her. If you don't have the time (and one meal can take an hour or two) see if a home health aide or a local volunteer can help.

◆ To avoid choking, your parent should eat sitting up, if possible, take small bites and avoid talking while eating.

In the Driver's Seat

Anyone who has followed a snail-paced car or one that darts past stop signs knows that plenty of older drivers shouldn't be on the roads. Studies show that the elderly have more car accidents per miles driven than other age groups. As we age, our reflexes slow, our peripheral vision narrows, our night vision dims, our eyes can't follow moving objects well and we become less coordinated. Medications and illness only compound the hazards.

And yet, driving is a way of life. Who can forget the exhilaration of turning sixteen and getting a driver's license? It was a ticket to freedom and a sign of maturity. To give up this mobility, and the independence it still represents, can be devastating for your parent. Even if she has no place to go or if ample public transportation is available, her driver's license and the car keys are a vital part of her life.

SAFETY BEHIND THE WHEEL

Depending upon the extent of your parent's limitations, you may be able to help improve his skills and keep him at the wheel a little longer. He won't take your advice readily: In fact, he is likely to be offended by it. But do it anyway. See if you can find a driving refresher course for senior citizens because that takes the hard work out of your hands (see box). If there is no such course in his area, tell him that you are concerned about his losing his license if he gets into an accident or gets a ticket—say that you know of other people his age who are no longer allowed to drive—and that in order to help him keep his license you need to address some issues and review a few matters together.

◆ Get your parent to wear his seat belt—both at the shoulder and at the waist. (Let him know that airbags and shoulder straps are not a replacement for safety belts that go around the waist.) Be sure that he can fasten and unfasten the belt easily. Automotive shops can adjust the shoulder strap so that it is comfortable or reset the belt so it can be more easily hooked and unhooked.

◆ Has your parent had his eyesight and hearing tested recently? If not, urge him to make the necessary appointments at once.

◆ If your parent suffers from dizziness, confusion or blurred eyesight, all of which affect driving, ask

A DRIVING REFRESHER

Your parent can take a refresher course in driving (which, as a bonus, will qualify her for a lower insurance premium in most states). The National Safety Council (800-621-6244) and the American Association of Retired Persons (800-424-3410) offer such courses. Senior centers, local AAA offices, driving schools and the Department of Motor Vehicles should have information about other driving courses in your parent's area.

Some of these groups also issue information and brochures that you might obtain and then casually leave on your parent's coffee table. The AAA Foundation for Traffic Safety (800-305-7233) offers several good publications, including a guide for families, a self-exam for older drivers and a fitness booklet aimed at improving the driving abilities of older people.

the doctor about ways to reduce these symptoms. They may be caused by untreated illness or inappropriate medications.

♦ Urge your parent to exercise, which will improve his reaction time, his range of motion and his attentiveness. Simply stretching the neck each day by rotating the head side to side and up and down, and circling the shoulders can help people twist around to parallel park or check oncoming traffic with greater agility and safety.

♦ Make sure that the car is in good working order—including brakes, defroster, defogger, battery, wipers, dashboard light and exterior lights and turn signals.

♦ Install large mirrors and add extra mirrors if your parent is having trouble turning his head to see what's behind him.

♦ If your mother cannot see clearly over the dashboard, buy a seat cushion at an automotive store. (Don't use a pillow because it might slip.) Automotive stores also sell gadgets to raise the pedals.

♦ If your parent is buying a new car, opt for power everything—brakes, seats, steering, locks, etc.

♦ Once on the road, your parent should avoid driving:

- at night, dawn or dusk
- during rush hour
- on unfamiliar routes
- in city centers or busy streets
- long distances
- in bad weather
- when he's not feeling well.

♦ Throughout all this, begin to wean your parent away from his automobile. Introduce him to carpools and public transportation or offer to drive him yourself, if possible. Do it in such a way that your parent can save face. Make it possible for him to bow out without feeling embarrassed.

WHEN IT'S TIME TO QUIT

When your parent is too ill, frail or disoriented, or when you decide that it's not safe for your children to be in the car with Grandpa, you need to act. Get him off the road. Unfortunately, you can't rely on the state to monitor his driving because most states, reluctant to alienate a large population of elderly voters, refuse to retest or otherwise restrict older drivers. Don't put this off. It's a matter of your parent's safety as well as the safety of others. It truly is a matter of life and death.

If you can't do it yourself, ask your parent's doctor to tell him that it's time to stop driving. It will be easier for your parent to hear *and* heed this if it comes from a doctor or another professional. If you decide to take it on, brace yourself, because your parent is bound to be hurt if not irate. Be sensitive to the gravity of what you are suggesting, to the implications, both practical and emotional, but remain firm in your resolve. And be ready with solutions to his travel problems—look into public and senior transportation programs, and ask family and friends if they can provide some transportation. If your parent uses his driver's license for identification, call the Department of Motor Vehicles to request a photo ID card.

If you don't make any progress, you can report an unsafe driver to the DMV or your state licensing agency. It's a difficult step, but it may be your only choice. Before you report your parent, ask that your name be kept confidential and find out in advance what happens when someone is reported. The states have varying procedures.

Pumping Iron

Even if your parent can't hobble across the hallway or push herself out of a wheelchair, she can still benefit from a little heave-ho, one-and-two. Don't be overprotective here. *But my parent is really too old and too sick for this.* If she can't lift weights or go to a senior swim class, maybe she can walk to the mailbox, sway to her favorite music or sweep her own front step. If she is confined to a wheelchair or a bed, she might do a series of neck rotations, arm stretches and foot flexes each day. Pretty much everyone can do something. Yes, even *your* parent.

BEFORE HE BEGINS

If your parent embarks on any exercise regime, he should first talk with his doctor, a physical therapist or a sports medicine specialist. Any weight training should be done with an experienced trainer.

WHY BOTHER?

Much of the physical decline that we attribute to old age is actually due to inactivity. By exercising, your mother can slow and maybe even reverse the effects of time, making her feel years younger, and giving her greater mobility, independence and energy. Exercise can reduce arthritis pain, boost immunity, enhance sleep and even improve memory.

A number of recent studies have demonstrated the vast benefits of flexing, lifting and stretching, even very late in life. In one study, a group of frail nursing home residents in their 80s and 90s worked out for ten weeks in a highly supervised program of weight lifting. These patients, many of whom had been written off as barely mobile, dramatically improved their strength, muscle mass, walking speed and stair-climbing abilities. Some gave up their canes and walkers. Others found they could climb stairs or get out of a chair without help for the first time in years. A second study of more than two thousand elderly people found that exercise reduced the risk of falls by 13 percent. Tai chi, a Chinese martial art that emphasizes balance, was found to be the most helpful. Those practicing tai chi lowered their risk of falls by 25 percent.

Once again, the old adage proves true: Use it or lose it.

THE RIGHT EXERCISE PROGRAM

A good exercise regime has three components: aerobic, strength

WALKING FOR LIFE

Walking is a great form of exercise for an elderly person. It's easy on joints. It's entertaining. It's cheap. And it can be social. It requires no special skills and can be done virtually anywhere. Your parent might just walk to the end of the driveway and back. Or for more serious walking, schools often have outdoor tracks and some malls are open during certain hours just for walkers. (Scenic routes are more enjoyable, but he should avoid wooded paths where rocks, roots and stumps can trip him up.)

Get him to start with a short walk, which may be a few paces or a few miles, depending upon his abilities, three times a week, and then add a little more each week. If possible, he should pick up the pace from a leisurely stroll to a more determined stride. As he walks, he should stand straight, with his head erect and arms swinging loosely at his sides. Tell him to lift his feet rather than shuffle, so he doesn't trip on cracks and bumps.

Your parent should drink plenty of liquids so he doesn't dehydrate. And he should drink *before* he's thirsty; once he's thirsty his body is already seriously low on fluids.

Buy your father comfortable sneakers with arch supports and thick rubber soles. Find sneakers made of nylon, mesh, canvas or other material that lets the air circulate. He should wear layers of clothing that he can shed as he warms up. If he needs to carry things with him, get him a fanny pack.

Someone should always know where he is headed, and he should keep to well-populated, safe areas.

and flexibility exercises. If your parent is able to move about (and remember those frail nursing home residents were lifting weights, so don't sell her short), she should alternate, doing aerobic exercise one day and strength-building exercises the next. Before or after each session she should do some stretching.

◆ **Aerobic.** Aerobic exercise strengthens the heart and lungs and improves endurance. It requires working the muscles without interruption for at least 15 minutes. Walking, riding a stationary bicycle, swimming or water exercises (which are especially good for people with arthritis, osteoporosis or back, knee or hip problems) are all good choices.

◆ **Strength.** Lifting light weights is a great way of increasing strength, but your parent can also stand in a doorway and push against the door jambs, squeeze his palms together, let someone else act as an immovable barrier, or work against the weight of his own body, as in push-ups or sit-ups. If your parent is frail, he can keep repetitions simple—lift his shoulders slowly and lower them, make a fist and release it, and so on.

◆ **Flexibility.** Bending and stretching improve range of motion, alleviate arthritis and relieve tension. With the lack of use that comes with age, muscles and bones shrink, and tendons and ligaments fail to extend. As a result, older people often stoop over, have trouble with their balance and experience back pain. Your parent should take it easy, stretching gently until he

---

❝When I was pregnant I did stretching exercises from a video, special exercises for pregnant women that were easy. My mother, who is in a wheelchair, would watch me. She enjoyed the music and energy of it. And it was something for her to do. I encouraged her to join in and, with some reluctance, she finally did. She did simple versions of what I was doing, or she would swing her arm out to the side when I was swinging my leg, that sort of thing. But she had fun with it.

After the baby was born and I wasn't using the tape anymore, I gave it to her. She says she still uses it most days. I know it helps her keep moving, and it's entertaining.**❞**

—JANE D.

feels a slight pull, then hold it for anywhere from eight to thirty counts, depending on how it feels, and then release it. He can stretch his fingers, rotate his head, arch his back, reach for his toes, raise his arms upward, pull his elbows back, lift his toes off the floor, and so on. Yoga classes are a great way to improve flexibility, and some are geared for seniors.

RULES OF THE GAME

No matter what exercise program is followed, an easy beginning, safe surroundings and a slow ending are especially important when the exerciser is aged. Your parent should be sure to observe the following guidelines:

◆ Rest whenever necessary. He should stop exercising immediately if he feels palpitations, chest pains or cramps, or if he becomes nauseated, dizzy, faint, light-headed, breathless or exhausted.

◆ Start slowly, and work up gradually, doing more each week.

◆ Begin and end with simple, easy stretches, warming up beforehand and then cooling down slowly toward the end.

◆ Stay in balance. Stand with legs planted slightly apart, back straight, body aligned and eyes focused ahead. Have something nearby that he can grab if he feels off balance.

◆ Don't exercise on an empty stomach or right after a big meal, but get ample fluids, especially if it's

VIDEO EXERCISE

A number of new videos offer exercises for older people, even those with disabilities. Try your local library or video store, or order one of your own.

"Armchair Fitness" by CC-M Productions (800-453-6280). The one-hour tape features gentle, easy exercises set to big-band music. Twenty minutes are done seated, for those who are less mobile. $39.95 plus shipping.

"55+ and Fit: A Life-Enhancing Stretch & Tone Program for Older Adults" by the University of Iowa (800-369-IOWA). This is for older people who are relatively fit and active. It's not aerobic, but requires the exerciser to get down on the floor and back up again for stretches. Fifty-five minutes long. $19.95 plus $4 shipping.

"Smile: So Much Improvement with a Little Exercise" by the University of Michigan, School of Public Health, Dept. of HB/HE, 1420 Washington Heights, Ann Arbor, MI, 48109. A thirty-five minute, low-intensity workout for frail elders. $15 for videotape; $7.50 for booklet.

"A Stroke Survivor's Workout" by Courage Stroke Network (800-553-6321.) An easy workout with lots of stretching for people who have had a stroke and have mild to severe mobility problems. $13.00.

"Exercising with Dorothy" by Stuart Choate, (800-779-8491). An easy, slow-paced workout for all elderly people, including those who use walkers or wheelchairs. $39.95.

---

a warm day (not ice-cold fluids, which can cause cramping).

◆ Avoid dizziness by not getting up too fast or changing directions too rapidly.

◆ Breathe regularly with each repetition. Inhale just before exertion and exhale at the maximum point of exertion. People tend to hold their breath when exercising.

◆ Choose a comfortable time of day, when it's not too hot or cold and the sun isn't too strong. If exercising outdoors, remember to apply sunscreen.

◆ Wear loose, comfortable clothing that doesn't impede movement, and wear layers that can be shed as the body warms up.

◆ Make exercising part of a daily routine. It's also helpful to keep a daily record of exercise—how many minutes, what movements, how many repetitions, etc.

◆ Do it to music, if possible.

♦ Do it with friends. If none are willing or about, join a class or gym. Exercising with others is more fun and is more likely to remain part of a routine.

♦ If exercising in the house, clear plenty of space to allow for safety and freedom of movement.

WHERE DO WE SIGN UP?

Find a community exercise program for elders which is oriented toward the special needs of your parent. It's apt to be a safe workout and it will add a nice social aspect to the sport. Call the local senior center, community center, department of recreation, Jewish center, YMCA or YWCA to find out about such classes. Ask local gyms and health clubs about exercise classes that might be appropriate. Don't forget to ask about yoga, tai chi and other forms of exercise that may be fun for your parent.

For those who choose to exercise at home, the American Association of Retired Persons (800-424-3410) puts out a free booklet called "Pep Up Your Life: A Fitness Book for Seniors," which describes a number of exercises with clear illustrations.

Staying Involved

Once you know your parent is safe, well-groomed and well-fed, what about feeding her mind and spirit? Stimulation and a sense of purpose will keep your parent's mind off her problems, boost her immune system and, quite simply, make life worth living. And what a relief it would be for you to know that your parent is enjoying her afternoons without you!

In this day and age of accessibility, even people with poor vision, no mobility or another disability can do quite a bit. If your mother is in a nursing home, she can still take up a new hobby, listen to books on tape or volunteer to help others in the home.

Your parent's real obstacle to activity may not be disability, but ageism and boredom. If you've ever been ill or between jobs, you know how boredom can lead to feelings of worthlessness. Having nothing to do, then feeling useless, leaves a person with no initiative to do anything. Over time, the idea of do-

❝*My father lives in a nursing home and he gets very bored and lonely. When anyone visits him, it's as though he won the lottery, he gets so excited. The rest of the time he basically sleeps and roams the hallways and talks to the nurses. He's not interested in any of the games or activities at the home and says all the other residents are 'too old' or half-crazy.*

I've tried a lot of things and I think my most successful effort was signing him up as a foster grandparent. This little boy, Tyler, not only visits, but sends him games and calls when he has homework questions. They've developed a really nice relationship.❞   —ELEANOR R.

ing something new becomes frightening. So if your mother doesn't want to do anything and is unhappy doing nothing, it's your job to push and prod. You may have to try a number of ideas before something strikes her fancy. Think about what she enjoys or used to enjoy in her earlier life. If she was always involved in local politics, for example, call local political offices to see if she can volunteer. Look through the newspaper, read bulletin boards and community calendars. Talk to her friends about what they are doing. Don't give up. You will find something. This section offers a few suggestions.

VOLUNTEERING

Volunteering is a wonderful way for your mother to regain a sense of purpose, to meet new people of different ages, to take her mind off herself and to be involved in things —politics, the arts, children, medical care, women's issues—whatever interests her.

Even if she can't leave the house or her bed, she may be able to make phone calls, offer advice, stuff envelopes or help in other ways. If she is in a nursing home she may be able to give tours, answer visitors' questions, deliver meals or flowers, or visit patients in the infirmary. The local chapter of the American Association of Retired Persons should have ideas. The federal volunteer agency ACTION (800-424-8867) runs a Retired Volunteer Program and a Senior Companion Program. The National Council on the Aging (202-479-1200) can make re-ferrals to a local Family Friends Program, which trains older people to work with seriously ill or disabled children, homeless children and rural families.

To find out about other possibilities call churches, synagogues, senior and community centers, hospitals, libraries, schools, foundations, grass-roots organizations, day-care centers, fund-raising groups, political campaigns, local museums, theaters, nature centers, the United Way and the Red Cross.

WORKING FOR PAY

If your parent doesn't want to work for free and she is relatively healthy, she may be able to find a job that pays. More and more shops and restaurants, for example, are finding that older people are more reliable and harder-working than teenagers, and some senior organizations specifically look to hire older people. The area agency on aging should also know of local employment programs for seniors. Also, look through the want ads or call some businesses that interest your parent—a museum gift shop, a children's clothing store, a movie theater.

LENDING A HAND

In earlier days you may not have wanted to bother or burden your parent by asking for favors. Well, now is the time to ask. If your parent is bored, give her a project—not a time-passer but something that would really help you. Ask her to sort through old photos, write addresses on all those holiday greet-

SPIRITUAL NEEDS

As a person's life heads into its last stages, questions about mortality and the meaning of life take on a new importance. Whether or not your parent practiced a religion, she might like to go to church or synagogue, attend a religious discussion group, speak to a member of the clergy or have someone read to her from the Bible or other religious books.

It's quite possible that she may be embarrassed to bring this up with you, or she may not even think of it unless you suggest it.

ing cards, look something up in the library for you, or otherwise help you in your personal or business life. You get a task done and she gets to feel useful.

EXERCISING THE MIND

It's never too late to learn new things. Call local colleges, community centers, high-school extension programs and art museums about classes and lectures. If your parent is relatively well, she might learn to paint with oils, cook Italian food or play the piano. Perhaps she wants to study classical music or learn about modern architecture. Through an organization called Elderhostel (617-426-7788), colleges, universities, museums, theaters and nation-

al parks offer special low-cost, short (usually about one week) courses for people who are over 60. (This usually involves travel, so it's only useful for those elders who are relatively independent and mobile.)

Find out about tours of museums and art galleries, many of which have special programs and prices for the elderly. For her next birthday, buy your parent tickets to the ballet, theater or opera.

Chronic illness and bed rest can stifle your parent's mind and make her listless. If your mother is ill in bed, but still mentally able, encourage her curiosity in the world beyond her. She can read about foreign places, study history or learn about anything that sparks her interest. If she can't read anymore, get her books and lectures on tape or videotapes from the local library. She doesn't have to take it all in—there are no exams—but learning gives a person optimism and pride.

TRAVEL AND OTHER EXPLORATION

If he's mobile, your parent should find out about tours—senior citizen or otherwise—to foreign countries or nearby cities, colleges, botanical gardens and historic sites and monuments. You may even want to join him. (Some tours don't require any walking, if your father would rather ride.)

Most senior centers offer discount trips, from day trips to weekend foliage tours to full vacations. Colleges and special-interest organizations, like museums, environmental groups and history clubs,

---

A RIDE IN THE COUNTRY

If your parent is very frail and doesn't get out much, he will benefit from a change of scene. Even if it takes some logistics to get him into the car, try it. Driving down a country road, by the sea or along a busy city street may cheer him up considerably. If you don't have time for pleasure trips, take him with you when you run your errands, just to get him out of the house.

---

often offer tours. And travel agents can book trips that are specially designed for older people or people with disabilities.

VIDEOTAPES AND BOOKS

If your parent can't get out or just likes to stay at home, get her some books and movies. She may not have the initiative to do this for herself, but once she is involved in a good story, she may get lost in it. How about some of her favorite old films? If she is active, get her to start a book club, with friends gathering once a month to discuss a book they have all read, or she might get some friends together to see a weekly movie at home.

If your parent has trouble seeing or can't read for some other reason, get books with large print or books on tape. Your local library, the Library of Congress at 800-424-8567, the American Foundation for the Blind at 800-232-5463 or the National Association for the Visually Handicapped at 212-889-3141 can help. Or buy a closed-circuit television that magnifies words, or see if there are local volunteers who read to older people.

PROJECTS AND HOBBIES

Maybe your parent isn't into making birdhouses, but what about other hobbies and projects, like gardening, bird-watching, collecting, model-building or painting? You never know what he will find fun. Think small-scale. If he doesn't want to take care of a full garden, he can have a few small planters in a window. It will give him something to tend to and learn about, and something that will grow and bloom. If he can't get about, put a bird feeder

---

"*The thing my mother loved most was music. The Jewish home where she lived had concerts and even a 'music therapy' class, but she couldn't go because she was afraid of riding in the elevator by herself and the nurse said there wasn't enough staff to escort her. One day I ran into the woman who directed the program in the hallway. I told her about my mother and she said she would be happy to bring Mom to and from the class each day. It was such a relief. Her spirits seemed to pick up right away.* **"** —BARBARA F.

near the window so he can watch the different birds from a comfortable seat. If his interest grows, buy him a pair of binoculars or a bird-guide for his birthday. Ask what sorts of things he used to do in his younger days; he might enjoy picking up an old hobby. If he doesn't want to do things on his own, ask at senior centers about hobby clubs and see if he doesn't have a few friends or neighbors who might like to explore a new subject or start a project with him.

SPORTS AND GAMES

Sports and games are a terrific way to exercise, meet people and build some confidence. It might be bingo, bridge or shuffleboard, or it could be walking, golf, cross-country skiing or swimming. Your father may have to take it easy, but that doesn't mean he can't partici-

---

SIMPLE PLEASURES

If your parent is severely ill, heavily medicated or suffering from confusion, it may take very little to entertain him. Games, like checkers or Go Fish, an otherwise simple task like sticking labels on envelopes, stroking a cat or listening to the jingle-jangle of children's songs may give his day a boost. What might seem simple to you may engage or even delight him.

---

pate. Some other activities to consider: fishing, horseshoes, darts, bowling, croquet, badminton, archery, miniature golf, camping or paddle tennis. Again, local senior centers may arrange or know of such events, or call the local department of recreation or community center.

SENIOR CENTER ACTIVITIES

Senior centers and adult day-care centers offer elders a place to socialize, talk about the events of the day, attend lectures, go on trips, learn new skills, and, in some cases, find out about practical matters like estate planning and budgeting. If there is more than one center in the area, your parent is welcome to sign up for classes at any or all of them.

SOCIALIZING

Calling other people is hardest when you need them the most, and if your parent is recently widowed, or just not used to socializing on her own, then initiating a new friendship or activity is difficult. She may need a little push from you. Urge her to call a potential friend or an acquaintance for lunch, a pot-luck supper, a movie, a ball game or a museum tour. It's often easiest to set up standing dates—a bridge game every Tuesday night, for example—so she doesn't have to think about creating new social events each week. If you don't get anywhere, maybe you can make the first effort, bringing your mother and one or two others together for

CREATURE COMFORTS

What has come to be known in medical lingo as pet-facilitated therapy, or PFT—basically, having a dog or cat—seems to boost people's emotional state as well as their physical health, according to several recent studies. Animals make us feel loved and less alone, and also give us a sense of responsibility. And, since Rascal needs a daily walk, a pet provides a little exercise as well. For someone who is anxious or agitated, stroking a pet is calming. The findings about "pet-facilitated therapy" have been so conclusive that federal law now mandates that elderly people living in subsidized housing be allowed to keep pets, so don't let the landlord shoo Patches or Felix out the door.

dinner. They'd probably be delighted if you accompanied them, at least the first time.

CROSSING THE GENERATION GAP

If your parent has always been good with children, he can still have them in his life. His involvement can enrich them and make him feel young again. Call local schools and day-care centers to find out about ways your parent might get involved. Look into foster grandparent programs or talk to a child you know about adopting your parent as a grandparent. If your parent is going to day care, some programs are intergenerational, mixing seniors and toddlers. The ACTION Agency (800-424-8867) runs a Foster Grandparent Program.

REMINISCING

The next time your father drifts back several decades and tells you stories you've heard before, rather than shake your head in resignation or despair, encourage him to tell more. He's doing something that's healing. Reminiscing allows him to review his life, think through important issues and digest it all. More important, it returns him, temporarily, to a time when he was younger, stronger, more confident and more capable.

If you can get your parent to tell new stories or flesh out the old ones, reminiscing can be a wonderful experience for you too. Or your children might like to share this activity with their grandparent. Exploring these details gives you insight into your parent's life and background, and it may be one of the last chances you have to learn about your heritage.

Tape-record your father's tales because you are sure to forget important details or a tone of voice that made the story his. Ask about his own life as well as his views of historical events he witnessed. What was his childhood house like? What about the school he attended? What were his parents like? What girls did he

“Dad and I always had what I call a business relationship. We talked about finances and health and practical matters, but never emotions and that sort of thing.

Then one day I was visiting him in the hospital and running out of conversation and, for some reason, I asked him about a girl he dated in college. I guess I had heard her name somewhere. Well, his eyes got misty and he started telling me all about being in love for the first time and the college parties and how hurt he was when she left him. He got lost in his past, lying in that bed, with tubes all over the place. He told me about other women he dated, his friends, funny things that happened, and the day he met my mother.

He was like a kid, remembering all this stuff. And I was seeing, for the first time in my life, this very human and vulnerable and youthful side of my father.**”**   —ALICIA B.

date? How did he travel or dress or cook as a young boy? Why did he chose his career? Does he remember the first time he saw a car or a plane? What Presidential elections were most exciting to him and why? What was life like for him during the Depression? Where was he during World War I or World War II?

Get your parent to talk about your ancestors. Draw a family tree together, gathering the additional information you need from other relatives. Find out where you came from and what those long-ago people were like. This is invaluable information that you can call on in resolving your own life and relationships—are there familiar patterns?—and pass down to your children and grandchildren.

As your parent talks, let him ramble about the subjects that he feels comfortable with. Don't correct him or force him to stay within some chronological order. Just listen, encourage him and enjoy it.